SO-BYN-043

Figure Treatment

BEAUTY GUIDE 2

Figure Treatment

Ann Gallant

F.S.H.B.Th., Int.B.Th.Dip., D.R.E. (Tutor),
Teacher's Certificate in Further Education

*Formerly Lecturer Responsible
for Beauty Therapy at
Chichester College of Higher Technology, and
Gloucestershire College of Art and Technology*

Stanley Thornes (Publishers) Ltd

First published in 1985 by
Stanley Thornes (Publishers) Ltd,
Old Station Drive,
Leckhampton,
CHELTENHAM GL53 0DN

British Library Cataloguing in Publication Data

Gallant, Ann
    Figure treatments. — (Beauty guides; 2)
    1. Beauty, Personal
    I. Title   II. Series
    646.7'2   RA778

    ISBN 0–85950–214–7

Typeset in 10/11 Garamond
by Tech-Set, Gateshead, Tyne & Wear.
Printed and bound in Great Britain
at The Pitman Press, Bath.

Contents

Acknowledgements

My thanks go to my husband, Robin Cleugh, who worked with patience and skill to provide all the photographs in this practical guide — making it so much more usable to the beauty practitioner working in the field. Thanks also to Angela Lumley for her care in the line drawings and sympathetic approach to the subject. For my daughter Patsy's forbearance in acting as a model for the photographs, I'd like to record a special mother's appreciation.

1

Starting a figure treatment service

The increasing use made by the general public of health and figure improvement facilities has brought about tremendous growth in the figure treatment area. Many salons have utilized previously unused or wasted space and now offer figure treatments among their other services. Combined use of reception facilities, both for treatment advice and promotion, and for related cosmetic sales, can increase the efficiency and use of the staff available as well as increase the overall turnover.

Expert guidance should be sought prior to setting up figure treatment services with regard to the best use of space available and the equipment required, as a different approach to figure treatment therapy is necessary compared with facial therapy or hairdressing. This is due to the higher initial costs of starting the service, and the

'BEAUTY GALLERY' — A COMPLETE SYSTEM OF TREATMENT

increased costs of both the treatment applications and the qualified staff required. Over-stringent economy in space or fittings may defeat the whole project, due to the natural association clients have of beauty and luxury which they expect to find when they come for treatment.

The limitations of the building available and the range of treatments likely to be the most popular should be balanced to achieve the best use of space. Care in the initial planning certainly pays off later in terms of the treatments possible, and able to be accomplished without overcrowding or delays in treatment. Building restrictions concerning fire risks and the necessary fire escapes should be checked with local authorities or planning officers before major plans are established. Full information and guidance is normally available from the equipment manufacturers, who also provide the necessary details required for submitting for a change of use of premises, or when extending premises, such as adding a body treatment service. Larger companies will negotiate with planning authorities in cases of difficulty, particularly in the case of large saunas, plunge pools or sun beds being installed, which are restricted in certain areas due to local health or safety laws.

HEALTH AND BEAUTY CLINIC

The possibilities of treatment cover a wide field in body therapy, there is some remedial work but the vast majority involves simple figure re-shaping and figure improvement. Research should be undertaken to discover which aspect of treatment is likely to prove the most popular and readily accepted by the local population. The situation of the clinic, within an urban, rural, or mainly residential area, and the age-range of the possible clients will dictate to some extent the best treatments with which to start. Flexibility is very important in the initial stages of building up a figure or full therapy service, as rigid treatment and equipment planning does not permit expansion in some areas, and re-assessment of others at a later stage in the business development, when the need for change becomes evident. A progressive approach seems to be the most successful, with the initial expenditure covering basic needs, such as saunas, showers, steam baths, plinths, etc., and with highly specialized equipment being added at a later stage, or as soon as the demand is apparent. Space is often more of a problem to acquire than the cost and installation of large scale apparatus, and so this is an important point when considering new premises. Body therapy always needs more sheer space than anticipated, and soon begins to feel overcrowded when the treatment areas are fully booked. The correct proportion of resting space to treatment cubicles is also very relevant, as space has to be given to clients who simply want to use the saunas, sun beds, etc., and do not want or cannot afford the time or money for more individual treatments. Though these self-help clients appear to take up clinic space without a great increase in clinic revenue, they can make the difference between running salon heating units such as the saunas at a loss or a profit, and so they should be planned for if space permits.

In countries where a licence to trade is required, inspection of facilities and staff qualifications is thorough, to ensure minimum standards are maintained to protect the consumer. This should work to the advantage of the well run and fully equipped clinic, and help to stop malpractice and misuse of premises, which still occur even with strict controls in force.

STARTING A BODY TREATMENT UNIT

Building a busy and profitable body treatment unit relies to a large extent on initial planning of the clinic, so that it appears attractive to the client. It should be well set out, clean, luxurious, and inviting to enter. Luxury and good hygiene are two factors clients expect and are used to within their own home, so use disposable items wherever possible to create the best impression. Paper sheeting, even if used over luxury towelling, confirms to the client that the working position is really spotless, and gives a very nice touch to the treatment, which inspires confidence.

If both male and female clients are to be catered for, the decor should be stylish and not over-feminine, with plain rich colours, wood finishes, and perhaps vinyl or marble effect floors for easy cleaning. Easy-care finishes are essential near sauna or shower areas, due to the condensation created, and because of the effects of the sustained heat on fabrics, etc. Surfaces which are easy to keep clean and so prevent mildew or bacteria from forming are more important with body therapy than the actual look of the finish, with wipe down surfaces being planned for wherever possible.

Help from an independent planning service is useful, or from the equipment firms. Experienced therapists are often the best guides when setting up a new clinic, as they will have a very good idea of which treatments achieve the best results and will therefore sell themselves to the clientele. The well known money earners — muscle contraction (faradism or interferential systems), vibratory and vacuum massage, galvanic cellulite systems and manual

'BEAUTY GALLERY' WITH GALVANIC UNIT — FACE AND BODY TREATMENTS

4

massage, used in combination with heating routines — are the ideal starting treatments in body therapy. These in combination with suntanning treatments (when permitted within the country), heat therapy from lamps, waxing, and hydrotherapy, cover the great majority of clients' problems. Naturally, the more highly qualified and experienced the therapist is, the greater will be her treatment range, and her need for specialized apparatus. With experience she will be capable of promoting and completing successfully a range of remedial applications, such as postnatal routines, mobilization of the muscles after inactivity, etc., all of which are under direct medical guidance.

HEAVY DUTY VIBRATOR

SOCIAL ASPECTS OF TREATMENT

Where the social aspects of the treatment are important, and the routine is mainly enjoyed for its relaxation and leisure aspects, the layout can be designed to encourage this to the full. Communal saunas, steam rooms and exercise areas all encourage participation and are much more profitable if well used, with no area lying idle and costing money. The layout of the body clinic should permit an easy client flow, and be designed to cope with larger numbers of clients in terms of clothes' storage, changing cubicles, resting areas, showers, etc., so that clients do not have to wait to use the facilities. Clever planning in the early stages, if a more social form of treatment is to be promoted, can insure that the maximum use is made of the space available. It is less easy to convert to this approach in treatment when a business is established.

5

Among male clients, group sessions seem to be most popular, with the comradeship appearing to enhance the value of the health and exercise routines undertaken. Younger women also seem to be more adventurous when in pairs, or small groups, and will motivate each other to succeed with their improvement plans. Treatments such as suntanning, muscle contraction and massage are very infectious to spectators, particularly as the results can be seen, and the clients are their own testimonial. They can act like instant advertizing if well handled, and without anybody being made to feel they have to have a treatment if it is offered.

Resting areas adjacent to the sauna suite can be fully utilized in this way with minor treatments being completed either in front of the other resting clients or in privacy behind curtained areas. Overhead curtain tracks can be installed which provide an open appearance when general space is needed but which also provide private cubicles instantly if treatments are decided upon. This flexibility is vital in body treatment, if the service is to be profitable.

Having once decided the treatment needed and how it should be applied, the more use that can be made of self-timing apparatus the better. The therapist's skill often lies in the choice of treatment, rather than in the actual application. Hydrotherapy baths and overhead solaria are examples of where the safety of the routine has been so improved that they can be used as self-treatment units, provided they are correctly set up initially by the therapist. This makes it possible for the therapist to plan the treatment, and set up the application, but then leave the client to apply it to herself. Equipment soon pays for itself on this basis.

The therapist is then free to concentrate on treatments that need her undivided attention, such as specific problems that have a high level of client anxiety connected with them. Naturally even some of the seemingly easy treatments could cause anxiety to nervous clients, so the therapist always has to make a decision regarding who needs help, perhaps even at the last moment prior to the application. This caring for the clients' well being, and awareness of any anxiety present, is an essential element of therapy, and must be built into any approach to body therapy if clients are not to be frightened away from trying treatments.

Even treatments like muscle contraction, with a high anxiety level, can be made more cost effective by encouraging clients to come in pairs, so that two treatments can be monitored together. With minds diverted in conversation, individual intensity levels can be increased, and more effective results achieved. The client then remembers the routine as a pleasant interlude, rather than as an unnerving experience. Clients who prefer privacy can also be

6

encouraged to have a grooming treatment completed simultaneously, such as eyebrow shaping, manicure, pedicure, etc., saving them time, and increasing profits to the salon.

Treatment planning to make the clinic as profitable as possible, while keeping the clients as satisfied as possible, is the most difficult aspect of running a successful body therapy service. It is an area that needs thought before even setting up the treatment area, or deciding apparatus and the applications to be offered.

Now the initial investment into body therapy is so large, pre-planning is vital and should be given the same kind of serious thought that any large business investment would warrant. Obtaining guidance from an independent clinic planning service — such as that offered by *Beauty Education International* — makes a lot of sense and saves costly errors in future clinic use.

BODY TREATMENT RANGE AND APPARATUS — TO OFFER A FULL BODY THERAPY SERVICE

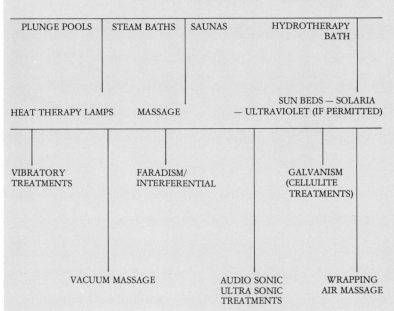

PLUNGE POOLS	STEAM BATHS	SAUNAS	HYDROTHERAPY BATH

HEAT THERAPY LAMPS   MASSAGE   SUN BEDS — SOLARIA — ULTRAVIOLET (IF PERMITTED)

VIBRATORY TREATMENTS   FARADISM/ INTERFERENTIAL   GALVANISM (CELLULITE TREATMENTS)

VACUUM MASSAGE   AUDIO SONIC ULTRA SONIC TREATMENTS   WRAPPING AIR MASSAGE

2

New equipment and treatment routines

With all the changes that are happening within the beauty therapy industry at present, now is a good time to take a searching look at existing equipment in the clinic, and consider not only its condition and performance, but its profitability as well. Many established and still effective systems of treatment have become superseded in popularity by more topical routines, which naturally enough receive more publicity and hence catch the client's eye and attention.

So to maintain a clientele in the face of competition, it may be necessary to come really up to date with the latest equipment. This provides an opportunity for linked advertising to show off the new system of treatment, and also provides an enjoyable excuse for some updating in training methods, by attending a short training course. This always helps to keep staff interest fresh and helps them to promote the new treatments confidently. Most of all, providing new equipment or techniques clearly demonstrates to the clients that you have their best interests at heart.

GALVANIC TREATMENT

The emphasis on improved, rather than completely new, systems of treatments shows clearly in the equipment available for sale or, in some cases, on rental at the moment. Many of the systems, such as galvanic iontophoresis, seem new but have in fact been in use for many years, particularly on the continent. Simpler apparatus, and availability of the negatively and positively charged ampoules in this instance, has increased the popularity of this treatment considerably. The ease of application with cellulite lotions for body galvanism has made the treatments less messy to apply, and improved their presentation to the client dramatically.

Galvanic treatment is available for facial desincrustation and facial and body iontophoresis, through a range of units from very simple to extremely complex. Sometimes galvanism is combined with muscle contraction in the form of interferential frequencies,

where they are used after muscle contraction treatments to reinforce the overall effects. These complex and advanced units provide a full range of body therapy services, but need to be well used to justify their initial expenditure.

GALVANIC TREATMENT

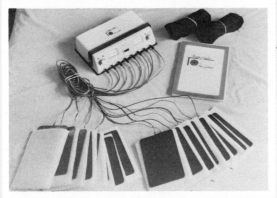

(a) Full body treatment of cellulite provides fast, effective and profitable results for the clinic

(b) With eight outlets (16 pads) many cellulite problem areas can be treated at once

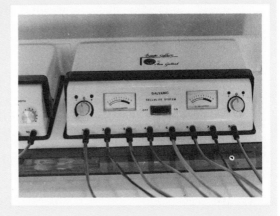

(c) The cellulite treatment is very popular with clients as it gives them the results they want

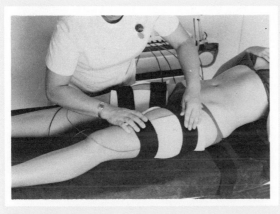

9

In fact, some treatment units are so comprehensive that they can encompass a large part of the total treatment and reduce the need for additional equipment, which can be a space saving if space is limited for offering the body service. The units are designed to provide standard muscle contraction, treatment of oedema and fluid fat (cellulite), as well as iontophoresis and desincrustation. So a large variety of problems can be treated if the equipment is correctly used. Many such units are under-used due to lack of knowledge of what they can achieve with careful application and correct choice of routine. Full training should be undertaken before embarking on such advanced applications within the salon.

COMBINED TREATMENT UNITS

Combined treatment units are becoming widely available and are usually in a trolley form, so apart from appearing very attractive, are a space saving — an asset when space is at a premium. Equipment is also available in a suitcase form, which is useful for visiting purposes. Small units can in this way provide spray toning, high frequency, vacuum massage, and with some units, galvanism for facial use.

Viewed separately, the elements of the combined facial or body units certainly appear very good value when brought together into their trolley form. In some cases the facial units also provide for magnification and steaming, alongside the classic high frequency, muscle contraction, vacuum suction and vaporizing systems. The most recent units, such as the *Beauty Gallery* system, sit on a

THE 'BEAUTY GALLERY' WITH ITS FARADIC MUSCLE CONTRACTION AND BODY GALVANIC CELLULITE SYSTEMS

(a)

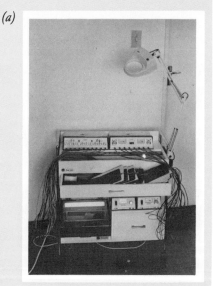

(b) The faradic system ten outlet (20 pad). Body straps (14), guide to muscle contraction

(c) The faradic unit:
ten outlets, individually controlled,
on/off, pulse control,
depth control,
ready light,
pulse light

trolley base, so an individual choice can be made to suit personal requirements. The system chosen for treatment can be positioned exactly where it can be seen and controlled accurately, whether it is muscle contraction or galvanism (for passing active substances through the skin during cellulite treatment).

With the combined units the therapist is able to move swiftly from one element of the treatment to another without inconveniencing the client, and is able to accomplish more in the allocated time. Even if commencing with the simpler combined facial units, giving pulsed air massage, brush cleansing, and vaporizing, time is saved in treatment. Further applications can then be added as needed, such as high frequency and galvanism and muscle contraction. It is a question of deciding carefully which treatments are really needed, and could be introduced within the clinic, rather than simply choosing a unit because it is impressive. Any unit of this type which is not fully used, is expensive to have taking up space within a cubicle. A lot depends on the therapist's skill in diagnosis, and her competence in applying the applications in the correct combinations to achieve results.

All the standard systems of treatment can of course be bought individually from many equipment manufacturers, and a range of treatments built up gradually, when the potential of the business is known. The better equipped the clinic is, however, the greater will be the variety of routines that can be offered so that something is available for all age-ranges, beauty requirements and tastes.

Having different systems of treatment available as separate pieces of equipment does have some advantages in a busy clinic, even though it never looks quite as impressive as mounted units. Separate units can be utilized by more than one therapist, and where the routines rely greatly on manual techniques rather than apparative work, individual units can be moved around to achieve maximum usage.

The *Beauty Gallery* system provides the best of both worlds, being impressive and easy to use, while allowing for independent use of the machines which permits maximum usage. The equipment is not tied to the system but can be used whenever it is needed, increasing its earning power for the clinic. Body systems available at present include the faradic ten outlet muscle contraction unit, the body galvanic cellulite system (with eight outlets — 16 pads) and the facial/body galvanic system which has two outlets — 4 pads — for treatment of cellulite.

PULSED VACUUM MASSAGE

Although not a new method of treatment, *pulsed* vacuum massage has become a popular method of body treatment, particularly when linked electrically with faradism to give a simultaneous application. Used as an addition to the normal gliding method of vacuum massage, static pulsing provides a concentrated stimulatory effect in a problem area. As this effect is achieved without physical effort on the part of the therapist, the treatment is a very useful addition to the body therapist's range of routines. It does

PULSED VACUUM MASSAGE

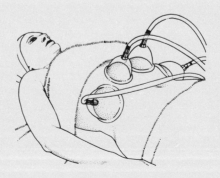

permit short periods of rest for the therapist, between the more manual elements of body therapy, and like muscle contraction routines combines well with manual applications to achieve results for the client.

The pulsing vacuum has many different applications and is most effective on established adipose deposits, or to speed the removal of subcutaneous fat that has been recently acquired and is being lost through a reduction diet. The static pulsing system must be preceded by the gliding vacuum method, and also concluded by it, to maximize the lymphatic drainage effects.

THE TREATMENT COUCH/WORKING POSITION

Rather a neglected area till recently, the actual working position and comfort of the client while undergoing treatment has now attracted more attention, and several new beds are available. The standard massage plinths are still an excellent way to begin developing a body care service, as they provide the necessary support for manual massage, to ensure the client gains the most out of the relaxation routine. Well built and stable models are available in wood and metal frames, and are capable of years of heavy and constant use. The size and solidness of the plinth should be considered if constant use is necessary, as within a health clinic or hydro situation. If electrical therapy is to form a major part of the treatment range, it is advisable to choose a well padded couch, and use a towelling cover over it. This helps to cut down on static electricity build-up which might be discharged during treatment, causing discomfort to both the therapist and the client. Muscle contraction routines and indirect high-frequency massage applications are treatments which suffer from this static electricity problem.

As the range of treatments grows within a clinic, it is possible to confine the manual routines to these basic working positions, and provide more padded and luxurious models for specific body treat-

MASSAGE COUCH AND STOOL

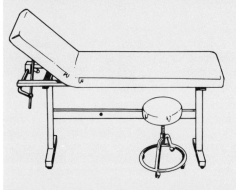

13

ment, such as muscle contraction, galvanism, heat therapy and suntanning with overhead solaria. Where the support and firmness of the working surface is not so critical to the success of the treatment, as it would be with manual massage, it is nice to be able to add to the comfort for the client, while they undergo some specific application.

These more luxurious couches can also be used for facial work, as they are multi-positional and sometimes even hydraulically controlled. Beds with hydraulic positioning seem luxurious to the standard conception of beauty therapy, but they are widely used around the world, especially in countries where selling the service to the client is based largely on her enjoyment of it. Client comfort is recognized more and more as an important factor for success in business, both for facial and body therapy, and it can make all the difference to a client's enjoyment of the treatment. Clients do tend to remember the stiff back they experienced after their facial routine, so it is worth thinking about investing a little more in a comfortable couch, particularly when refitting a clinic or expanding a business, or even when starting the initial business from stratch.

Chairs are available which permit a wide range of facial and body applications, by repositioning and using height extensions to bring the working surface up to a suitable height for body therapy. This means that one cubicle can provide for a wide range of routines without disturbing the client. Although expensive, this type of chair is very comfortable for the client, and a joy to work with for the therapist. It can be moved into a variety of different positions for facial work, electrology, waxing/pedicure routines, and body treatments, just by moving a couple of levers. Naturally one chair, however well thought out, cannot be expected to be ideal for every application, and the stability of these metal-framed chairs makes them a little less useful for manual massage, but perfectly suitable for all other forms of body therapy.

So when choosing a working couch make sure it is correct for its task, and not a compromise, and do not expect one unit to provide for everything. Make sure the couch or plinth is the correct working height for the individual member of staff, and if not, organize some means of improving their working posture, to avoid back strain. Couches these days are available in different heights, according to the manufacturer, so it is worth taking time to see and actually test out the height practically, rather than simply ordering the couch by post and then finding it is a poor working height.

Strength and stability are important with the massage plinths, comfort and luxury with the more general treatment couches, so try to decide the main areas of use when making the initial

purchase. Be prepared to pay a reasonable amount for such an important element of the treatment success, as one would for any facet of treatment destined to earn the clinic a high level of revenue. Apart from impressing the client, it is also a fact that if the client is comfortable they relax and make the therapist's work more effective and beneficial. Comfort for the therapist is another important consideration, as unless body posture is correct, backache can be a real problem which spoils or prevents regular and profitable work.

SUNTANNING EQUIPMENT

The latest feature on the tanning scene is the sun bed, which has proved to be extremely popular among clients. Placed in resting areas, or in separate cubicles, the beds soon recoup their initial purchase prices if well promoted, even though they are a large investment in terms of cost. They do take additional space in a clinic, because they cannot be used over a working couch as the overhead solaria can. But if the space is available, the novelty to clients certainly makes them worth while.

One of the latest ideas is to provide total body exposure, treating the back and front of the body at once. This feature halves the total exposure time and doubles the potential earnings of the sun bed so that it pays for itself more quickly. The newness of the sun bed coupled with the lack of sun in countries such as the United Kingdom, seems to have assured the success of this attractive method of tanning. Clinics should claim their rightful share of this market, in countries where it has potential, rather than letting it be gained by health centres and sports and leisure complexes, who are not slow to see its simplicity and application and strong public appeal.

Several features which increase the effectiveness of even tanning are worth considering, for example the length of the beds and built-in

A SUN BED

15

tubes if males are to be treated, as a few extra inches avoid having to tan the body in two sections, which is time wasting. Curved sides on the bed improves the all-over effect, and ensures the sides of the body become evenly tanned. The value of an overhead sun roof is obvious in a busy health clinic, allowing a faster client flow. Many clinics could save space by installing one bed with a sun roof, rather than two individual couches. It all depends on the clientele and the form the business takes, but there can no longer be the claim that space does not exist for these popular treatments to be installed.

Remember that the ultraviolet tubes for the sun beds have a definite life span and will decrease in their effectiveness or ability to tan after a time. Simple testing units are available from the sun bed suppliers. If the tubes appear to need replacement rather quickly, it probably indicates that they have been kept very busy in the clinic, earning revenue from being well used. The tubes have a set number of hours of perfect output, so it is well worth taking a note of when the beds are installed and when the lamps first need replacement and checking this against sun bed takings over the same period. They will always be found to have earned their keep — so change the tubes as soon as necessary to maintain a good service.

The replacement cost of the ultraviolet tubes makes it important to think seriously before buying a second-hand sun bed, as the entire replacement of the tubes makes up a large percentage of the total cost.

EQUIPMENT CHOICE

The range of available equipment is vast, and choice should be made on a careful assessment of what the clinic needs, and units obtained to match this need exactly. The common mistake in equipment purchase is to buy a unit that is incapable of fulfilling a task, is underpowered, or has too few outlets, as in muscle contraction, or galvanic cellulite routines. Once having bought a unit it is useless to say that it is incomplete, or too lightweight, or incapable of continuous use. Make sure this is found out before buying, to avoid disappointment. The most expert therapists are not embarrassed about asking searching questions of the equipment manufacturers, regarding their equipment. It shows their knowledge and experience, rather than lack of it.

Remember also that the equipment firms wish you to be satisfied with your purchase, so that you will return for further units, so ask their advice, ask searching questions and you will receive the right equipment for the job.

3

A total approach to body treatment

A total approach is the best method to adopt when starting or developing a body care service. This allows full profitability to be attained more easily, but does depend on a substantial investment initially, in terms of space, facilities, equipment, and availability of trained therapists. This approach relies on using all possible systems of electrical therapy, heat treatment, diet, exercise, etc., based on a detailed figure assessment. Details of the client's medical history, life style, as well as essential family details, are recorded initially, to avoid unsuitable treatments being completed.

FIGURE ASSESSMENT

Apart from taking details of the client's medical history, a figure assessment should be made and details of the client's measurements, weight and height, and any postural defects (such as round shoulders which need to be improved before general exercise is advised) should be noted. Permanent postural faults such as spinal curvature or knock knees also have to be recognized as they can alter or prohibit certain exercise routines. The medical background gives information on the client's general health, and indicates which treatments will be effective and safe to apply. Tactful questions may reveal a history of disc troubles, fluctuating weight levels, fluid retention, etc., which all have vital relevance to the treatment plan. Minor problems of varicose veins, thread veins, etc., or temporary conditions such as menstruation, sunburn, etc., alter treatment and must be noted on each visit.

MEDICAL LIAISON

Medical liaison is desirable for postnatal conditions, or obesity where a large weight loss is planned. If the client has not consulted her doctor for any reason for a very long period, and hence is unaware of the state of her health, then a general check-up is wise, and can avoid problems occurring. Both the therapist and the client feel more confident about starting the treatment routines, if they know all is well 'health wise'.

CLINIC PLANS

Small body treatment unit in conjunction with facial therapy clinic

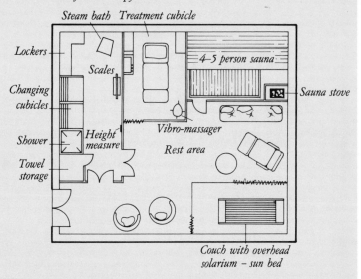

Steam bath
Treatment cubicle
Lockers
Scales
4–5 person sauna
Changing cubicles
Sauna stove
Shower
Height measure
Vibro-massager
Rest area
Towel storage
Couch with overhead solarium – sun bed

Health clinic/exercise studio

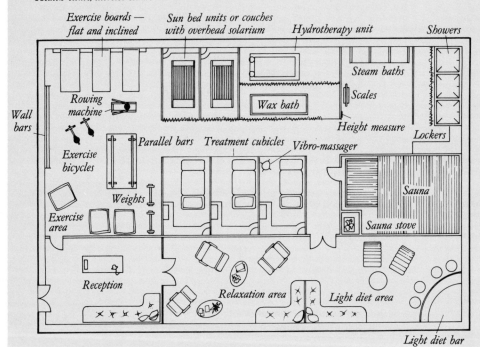

Exercise boards — flat and inclined
Sun bed units or couches with overhead solarium
Hydrotherapy unit
Showers
Steam baths
Scales
Rowing machine
Wax bath
Height measure
Wall bars
Lockers
Parallel bars
Treatment cubicles
Vibro-massager
Exercise bicycles
Sauna
Weights
Exercise area
Sauna stove
Reception
Relaxation area
Light diet area
Light diet bar

By extending into health-linked treatments, potential clients can be increased dramatically, and the effects of the routines are also satisfying. Preventative routines for muscular stiffness, weight control, and maintenance of general health are becoming increasingly important to the beauty industry and should not be ignored.

SPECIFIC REDUCTION

Much of the therapist's work is concerned with specific reduction, reshaping and toning up the figure, while reducing adipose deposits through linked diet advice. There are many ways these improvements can be accomplished, based on diagnosis and assessment of the body. If the problem is clearly loss of muscle tone, then muscle contraction routines can be used to reinforce the home exercise routines advised. However, if the problem is weight, rather than poor muscle tone, then diet and stimulatory treatments such as gyratory massage or vacuum can be employed to advantage, and the faradism (muscle contraction) would in this case be superfluous. If fluid retention seems involved, and is not receiving medical attention, then with medical permission treatments such as galvanic cellulite routines to increase biological function and remove unwanted intra-cellular infiltrations can be gradually applied to the area. Interferential muscle contractions for deep acting work on the tissues initially, and later on muscle toning, can also be successfully applied in this case. Many conditions described by the client as 'cellulite' need this approach in treatment, being abnormalities of the circulatory system. This is naturally backed up by elimination diets, deep massage of the affected areas, and increased general activity of the whole body to clear toxins from the system.

POSTNATAL ROUTINES

Postnatal routines are a special aspect of specific reduction, and require a skilful combination of treatments. The client normally has medical permission to commence treatment six to eight weeks after a normal birth, and will usually have a weight problem, over-extended abdominal muscles, flaccid breasts, and may have stretch marks. These stretch marks may be the most difficult part of the problem to remedy, and will be present on the upper thighs, lower abdominal area, and the breasts. Improved pre-natal products and new treatments for the stretch marks themselves, hold more promise for a solution to this disfiguring problem.

The postnatal treatment will include general fitness and relaxation aspects such as massage to bring the client back to full health and vigour, after the strain of the pregnancy and the actual birth. It will also concentrate on electrical muscle contraction, home exercises

to shorten the stretched abdominal muscles, and a diet to help shed the unwanted weight. Heat therapy, galvanic cellulite routines, vacuum and vibratory massage will all play a part in the programme to give variety, and to maintain client interest. This is important even with a strongly motivated client such as a postnatal one, who although she has many incentives to regain her figure, also has many other demands on her time, from the new baby and her other family commitments. So never underestimate the importance of encouragement, or variety in the treatment programme, it can make all the difference between success and failure.

OBESITY CONTROL

When a really overweight client is to be treated, several factors need consideration — the individual's health being of paramount importance, and also their capacity to reduce their size over a long period without problems. The personality of the individual and the incentives to reduce will give the therapist a guide to the likely success that may be achieved. If the weight loss has been medically directed, then it is more likely that clients will make a determined effort to keep to the diet plan, although they certainly do not find it any easier to reduce, even though for their health's sake they know they must. Men seem to show more determination on medically prescribed diet plans than women, perhaps they can place themselves more easily out of the path of temptation than women, normally not having to be involved with food preparation.

Long term obesity may cause physical problems such as high blood pressure, shortness of breath, or pain in weight-bearing joints to have become established. As these problems alter, and normally reduce in severity as the weight decreases, the individual's health requires monitoring, and so regular medical checks must become a standard part of the treatment plan. This is absolutely vital if the client's obesity has caused development of any real severe condition such as diabetes, or is associated with a heart abnormality such as angina pectoris. Weight problems are of course, a symptom of many actual systemic illnesses, and in this case the diet has to be prescribed medically, as part of the overall medical treatment and medication. In this case the therapist simply helps the client to keep to the diet and adapt it to their own life style and social eating pattern, but does not alter its fundamental structure. Even this interpretation of the diet, can make the difference between a successful reduction, or complete failure, as it is often difficult for ordinary people to understand a diet chart, and they find it very confusing to make sense of in relation to their normal food intake. The therapist can simplify the charts, and work out some simple daily plans using the medical diets as a basis, and present these to the obese client, as part of her expert work.

20

The client's medication may require alteration during the process of a really large weight loss, which perhaps takes a year to accomplish, so medical guidance is necessary, and can be very useful and informative to the therapist. A really large weight loss causes changes to occur in the body, most of them to the good, but all of which require a certain amount of adjustment, which the therapist can help with most effectively. Factors such as greater mobility in the body generally, ability to exercise without strain or loss of breath, and less strain on the joints, can be used by the therapist to develop a personal plan for the client's well-being. When excess weight is shed, the body is able to regain a normal state of health surprisingly quickly, and clients are often pleased to discover they have a capacity for exercise they had not expected.

Unless the obesity has been very long established and has caused actual damage to occur, for example within the joints, then the loss of weight seems almost like a miracle change as far as health is concerned. Even when joint damage is present, the reduction in the load to be borne causes a great improvement in the discomfort level experienced from aching hip, knee and ankle joints. So the body has a great capacity to recover from obesity, and this is a very good point to stress to clients, to give them an incentive to keep on the long term reduction plans.

Giving the obese client a weight loss goal that is possible to achieve, in a progressive fashion is also important for sustained success. To give a 103 kg (16 stone) client a goal initially of 57 kg (9 stone) is unrealistic and perhaps unkind, even though it may indeed be the correct weight for them. It is very likely to be doomed to failure right from the start, as the client may not feel able even to start the diet in the face of such a lot to lose. So give a goal that is attainable, within a reasonable time, of say 12 kg (2 stone) at each stage, and once having helped the client to reach this lower weight, give a new lower goal. In this way gradually reaching the correct target weight without the client becoming demoralized or giving up altogether — which does happen all too often if an overtough or inflexible approach is adopted.

While the client is reducing, and becoming gradually more active and healthy, the therapist must use every means available within the clinic to maintain client interest, and spur further efforts on the home diet and exercise programmes. Once the client's own movitation to improve their figure, health, and looks is aroused, the therapist then becomes not the motivator, but rather the adviser to the overall plan. This then helps the client on to the path of total re-education of their figure, and will help prevent real obesity occurring again. The obese person with a lifetime of acquired bad eating habits will, however, normally need the therapist's help to maintain their reduced size, and so will become a regular, satisfied and valuable salon client.

BUILDING THE BODY SERVICE

The therapist nowadays has to be adaptable, and offer what the client wants if business is to be fully exploited. The exclusiveness which previously had dominance, gave rise to the feeling that beauty treatments were only for the very wealthy or special people in the community, and were not for the average person who earned their living through their own efforts. If the beauty industry is to develop and grow, it has to re-examine its own image to discover why its services are not as fully used as they might be, particularly when the world wide interest in physical health is considered. Much of the potential business of beauty clinics is perhaps being lost to health centres, sports clubs, etc., simply because they have a far more open approach to the public, and are freely available. The image of exclusiveness has surely a lot to do with keeping health and beauty treatments for the small minority, rather than being widely enjoyed. Health clinics who promote their image well are busy and profitable, and offer a complete service to the client.

INFORMATION FOR THE BODY TREATMENT CARD

One of the first things to set up when establishing a body therapy service is a record card system, which acts as a reference for all the treatments completed, and gives essential details of the clients' medical and clinical records.

The record card prevents unsuitable or harmful routines being applied, if filled in correctly initially, and if referred to during the course of the treatment plan. Naturally it is necessary to know which treatments would be unsuitable by understanding the reasons for the contra-indications and how they relate to the individual. Taking the client's details down carefully is not enough; one has to be able to interpret them, to work out a safe and effective plan suited to the individual. Information derived from the card helps decide the best treatment plan to suit the client's family circumstances, and the best method of attendances to get results, without being difficult for the client to follow. The card can also indicate when changes in the clinic routine would be advantageous, if its details are read correctly. Changes in the home advice can also be prompted in the same manner, if the therapist is alert and using the card as her overall guide.

CLIENT ATTENDANCE

The record card acts as a detailed record of the client's attendance, and progress, if on a corrective or figure improvement, or reduction programme, where regular attendance is vital for success. If progress is not being made, or is slower than desired, then the

card can be used to discuss with the client the possible reason for lack of success. If concentrated attendance is needed, as in re-shaping programmes with muscle contraction routines (three times weekly being ideal), and the client has been unable to attend as frequently as needed, the reason for the lack of results can be explained frankly. Spasmodic attendance also shows up clearly on a record card, and again gives the possible reason for slow progress. Treatments that rely on regular attendance, must be honestly discussed initially with the client at the start of the programme, and their co-operation gained on the actual frequency of treatment, and the back-up home advice.

METHOD OF RECORDING INFORMATION

The actual method of recording the necessary information differs from clinic to clinic, depending on the range of treatments offered. Also, clients undertaking relaxation treatments rather than remedial programmes have no need of detailed measurements and weight records, and hence can simply have their attendances recorded on a very simple form of record card.

The card should provide for all the necessary information to be recorded, often in an abbreviated form for economy of space and to avoid the need for bulky filing systems within the clinic. Information should be kept as simple as possible, and only factors which actually relate to the treatment plan should be recorded. Commencing with a reasonable sized card which is capable of recording 25 to 30 treatments, with space for relevant measurements/weight losses if needed, makes for efficient business organization. This then provides for the client's medical history, past and present, height, bone structure and body type, the weight and measurements to be recorded initially. It also allows for periodic checks during the treatment plan of the altering factors, such as the weight losses and the cm/in reduction, to be shown.

These periodic checks of weighing and measuring should only be undertaken when it seems desirable in the therapist's judgement to encourage the client, or when a weight or size loss seems inevitable. It can be discouraging to the client to have every minute fluctuation of weight and size recorded, particularly as most women have increases in both weight and body measurements prior to each monthly period. These are due to the hormone influence present in the body at this time, which affects fluid retention, giving rise to oedema (swelling-fluid in the tissues). This gives feelings of fullness in the breasts, and abdominal distension. Women feel fatter at this time of the month, so do not need this fact confirmed by an unfeeling therapist. Better by far to explain to the client the reason for the changes, and give advice to help minimize the effects every month,

RECORD CARD

Body Treatment Card Name

Address				Tel. Work			
				Home			
Doctor	Medication			Smoke	Drink	Age	
Medical history	Number of pregnancies	Ages of children		Recent post natal examination			
Operations	Hysterectomy	Date		Caesarean section	Date		
General health	Good	Poor	Constipation	High blood pressure		Varicose veins	
Body condition	Overweight	Poor muscle tone		Underweight		Out of proportion	
Treatment plan	General reduction		Specific reduction				
	Massage/relaxation		Cellulite				

Treatments booked / Products used and advised
Treatments completed

Date		Date	

Diet plan Name:

Moderate protein/ low carbohydrate		Weight	
		Height	
Elimination diet		Measurements Date	
Moderate protein/low fat/ low carbohydrate		1 Bust, chest	
Carbohydrate unit diet		2 Waist	
		3 Hips	
		4 Thighs left	
		Thighs right	
		5 Knee	
		6 Calf	
		7 Ankle	
		8 Wrist	
		9 Upper arm	

Figure and posture faults

Rounded shoulders	Spinal curvature
Abdominal weakness	Cellulite on thighs
Adipose deposits on buttocks	Weak inside thighs
	Fluid on knees
Tension in upper back	Heavy lower legs

Exercise plan

through dietary controls to reduce the fluid retention, and exercise to tone the muscles in the most affected areas.

CLIENT ENCOURAGEMENT

Instead of confronting the client with all their small failures, try a more positive approach, by weighing and measuring at intervals to produce an overall trend which the client can see and relate to, and which encourages their personal efforts. Work with the client towards achieving a positive downward trend over the weeks/months involved, and encourage and praise individual results at every stage. Use the record card to discuss with the client any reasons for a static period in the reduction plan. If no evident reason presents itself, it may point to a need to change the programme, alter the diet, vary the actual treatments applied, or extend the exercise routines. All this should be done before the client gets despondent with their lack of results, and gives up in despair, breaking their diet and spoiling their progress to date. If therapists are in tune with their clients, and can sense when they need more support, or a change to maintain interest in the programmes, then they will find they can get the clients to provide their own results. This is real client handling in action, and the therapist's skill, plus the information that has been gained on the record card, can make this perfectly possible with the vast majority of clients. The therapist who appears able to get results with clients is the one who is good at client handling, and achieves client co-operation at every stage of the programme.

If an overall approach to improvement is being followed, it can even provide for a certain amount of flexibility in the reduction and reshaping plans, so allowing a modified social life to be built in. Using diets which are based on carbohydrate units (CUs), rather than calories, can be useful if the client has a social life to follow, and it would be more likely to ensure adherence to the diet plan advised. Many clients break diets because they are not suited to their life style, and hence are restrictive or just plain boring to follow. By careful questioning in the initial stages of the consultation, and recording the client's tastes and social life style on the record card, a diet which is likely to work can be devised.

MEASUREMENTS

Overall measurements, body type, postural problems, and any areas of particular worry to the client can be recorded initially. These facts are then considered carefully in order to plan the best treatment plan, as they will determine the sequence of events, both for home advice and clinical applications. They will also point out any contra-indications to treatment (reasons why the treatment may not be given).

Measurements need only then be recorded periodically with a large weight loss, perhaps only once or twice a month is necessary,

unless the client feels a need to hear their own losses, to confirm that they are succeeding. For clients undertaking intensive programmes of diet reduction, exercise routines, and specific reduction clinic applications, then weekly or even twice weekly measuring is important for success.

Specific reduction programmes, concerning reshaping, or improvement of one area of the body, need regular checking through measurements, but if the client is attending three times a week, then once a week is quite adequate for filling in the record card.

TAKING MEASUREMENTS

Measurements should be taken carefully, but quickly, and with due regard for the client's modesty. Measurement-taking need not be elaborate, but the actual measurements must be taken in the same place on every occasion. If different staff treat a client within the client's treatment programmes, ensure that all measure in the same way. It is quite possible to have one client measured by three different staff and to get three completely different sets of measurements because they have been taken in a slightly different place. Check that measurements are actually on the fullest part of the chest (or bust in women) or waist, or 10 cm (4 in) below the waist for the upper hip, or actually around the fullest part of the buttocks/lower abdominal area for example.

If several staff are involved, organize training sessions to ensure that everyone knows what is needed if accurate measurement records are to be obtained. For really large clients this may not be

TAKING MEASUREMENTS

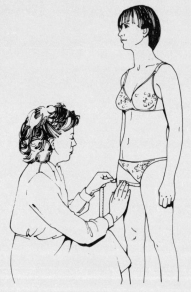

26

so important, as overall weight loss is desired, rather than reshaping, but for figure shapers it is vital. It can be very confusing, and depressing, not to be assured that the inches are going from the right rather than the wrong areas.

WEIGHT RECORDS

It is important that weight is recorded accurately, with or without the clinic gown, and in kg or stones and lb, whichever system is in operation in the country. Stick to one system of weighing, preferably one the client can understand, and which means something to them. If the country is in transition, perhaps from stones to kilograms (metric), use the new system for clinic purposes, but be prepared to convert the weight for the client's information, using a conversion chart for accuracy.

Use weight tables as a guide to weight loss, only if a sensible weight level is projected for the client's height, bone structure, etc., otherwise a realistic common-sense approach is best. If a client should be 50 kg (approximately 8 stone), but is never likely to attain or maintain this weight level, settle for 57 kg (9 stone), and be glad the client has been able to achieve this loss, and is no longer really overweight. If a client is to be healthy, and able to live a normal social life without feeling guilt ridden every time they eat, it is better to settle for a happy life, rather than for a starvation regime which makes the client a nervous wreck.

RECORDING THE CLINIC APPLICATIONS

The actual treatments completed should be recorded, in a brief form, for example: steam bath, S/B; massage, Mas; vacuum massage on the upper thighs, Vac Mas upper thighs; 10 min, etc. Muscle contraction routines need to have the areas of treatment recorded, the durations, the intensity needed to achieve contractions, and any special points relating to the treatment, such as client tolerance. Vacuum massage needs much the same type of record, giving reduced pressure levels, reactions, after-effects as guidance, and length of application times. Any special points that will act as guidance on future occasions should be recorded, such as a client's tendency to bruising with vacuum for example, or particular muscle tone condition in individual areas with faradism, which will indicate if progress is being made.

Any problems encountered during treatment should also be listed, particularly if staff changes are unavoidable, as the new member of staff treating the client has only the card to guide her on many occasions to the client's tolerance to an application. Any problems which might point to a need to change or adapt the treatment plan should be noted. An example being where large adipose deposits are present, on the buttocks or abdominal area, perhaps causing

27

discomfort in muscle contraction applications; this could point to the need for the more advanced systems of muscle contraction now available or for interferential methods of muscle contraction, where surface skin resistance is less of a problem due to the different principles of treatment involved.

Progress may also be recorded (apart from reduction progress, which is recorded in the weight/measurement sections of the card) in such clinic applications as heat therapy for muscular stiffness, mobilization of the body through exercise, and postural re-education or muscular rehabilitation after illness, weight loss or pregnancy. Improvements in muscle tone should also be noted, as these will not always show up as a change of measurement in an area. The improvement in the abdominal weakness of the rectus abdominis muscle after pregnancy shows as an improvement in tone, and strength as the muscle shortens, rather than as a cm/in reduction.

CONTRA-INDICATIONS

Any major contra-indications to treatment must be recorded at the start of the treatment plan, particularly if weight loss is involved and the client has to alter their dietary intake radically. Medical guidance must be sought in all cases of obesity or where the client has an established medical condition such as thyroid abnormality, angina pectoris, or suffers from high blood pressure. Many of these systemic conditions may be improved by the loss of unwanted weight, but it is essential that the client's doctor is aware of the treatment plan being undertaken by his patient. If this approach is used it is often found that the client is not contra-indicated to as much as might be supposed, and may be able to have some adapted routines which would have seemed impossible to the therapist at first. So use the guidance provided by the medical profession, and build on the advice given to create success-ful and safe routines.

Minor problems such as thread veins, sensitivity in the area, low tolerance to treatment, etc., should all be noted, as they will require that the treatment is adapted to avoid skin damage or discomfort. Systemic problems such as oedema should be noted, and checked medically if their cause is not known. Most treatment applications have some contra-indications, and they may differ from one routine to another, so the therapist must be aware of them all if clients are not to be damaged in any way. Many of the treatment routines are so effective these days that they are capable of causing real harm if used carelessly, so the therapist has to be aware of her responsibilities to the client.

With a good knowledge of the effects of the equipment, it is usually possible to devise a routine which avoids any problems created by

the client's contra-indications, and is still able to get results. This may be at a slower rate, but this is often the best way to get long lasting results, which the client is capable of maintaining after the conclusion of the treatment programme, perhaps with just a maintenance form of attendance.

THE RELATIONSHIP OF HEALTH, DIET AND EXERCISE TO COMBINED BODY PROGRAMMES

Any body treatments the therapist completes must take into account the overall health of the client, and their capacity for exercise. The client's weight also relates directly to diet, unless they have a medical problem as the cause (which is unusual, but must be tactfully found out). When a client is severely overweight, that is 20% or more over their correct weight for their height and build, they are classed as obese, and medical guidance is needed before a diet can be suggested. This diet may be devised by a physician, a dietician, or more commonly in Europe by a fully qualified beauty therapist.

So it is necessary to have a sound knowledge of nutrition in order to devise diet plans for clients or to interpret the medically prescribed diet the client has been given. In many cases all that is needed is the ability to transform the diet plan into a sequence of daily food plans which the client can understand and follow. It is easier for the majority of clients if the diet gives exact quantities of food, such as protein, carbohydrates, fats, etc., and is providing them with no opportunity for cheating on overall food intake. Any diet that allows the client to use their own discretion as to amounts or sizes of food portions, will find that the client quickly runs into difficulties, and either over-calculates or does not eat enough of the right elements and feels very hungry. So do not expect clients to be expert diet-planners or food assessors, that is the therapist's job, and one she has had special training to accomplish.

A DIET SHOULD SPECIFY EXACT QUANTITIES

29

DEVISING A DIET PLAN

In order to devise a diet which suits the client's temperament, personal food tastes, and life style, and thus is sure to be followed, some important points have to be considered:

(1) The client's existing energy (food) intake.

(2) The client's actual energy (food) needs, related to their basal metabolic rate (BMR), their age and the work they do.

(3) The proportional reduction of food (calories/joules) which will bring about a consistent body weight loss.

(4) The client's eating pattern and social life, which determines when the food is eaten, and how effectively the body uses its energy intake.

(5) The food preferences, which can be built into the diet whenever possible to ensure its success.

(6) Food combinations which can be adapted and improved upon to allow the body to gain more nutrients from the food, while reducing wasteful calories/joules.

(7) The cooking methods used in the food preparation, which can dramatically increase their calorific value, e.g. frying of fish in breadcrumbs or batter, as compared with grilling or baking it in the oven.

(8) Knowledge of actual food values in a calorific or energy requirements form, which can then be translated into a simple, easily-understood form for the client. Once the clients themselves can recognize wasteful calories, and re-educate their appetites to avoid these wasteful areas, they are on the path to successful weight control.

So the therapist has to know what the food is worth to the body (its energy-giving value), how much the client requires to fulfil their daily energy requirements (BMR) — and how an adjustment can be brought about which reduces the actual body weight, and then maintains it at the correct level.

The client's existing energy (food) intake, their food preferences, and their pattern of eating, all directly relate to the actual value of the food. If a client's preferences and life style indicate that daily calorie counting would be difficult or unrealistic for them to accomplish, then a weekly energy plan could be devised. This would permit a more stringent approach to the diet within the week, and allow for a little more flexibility and freedom over the social weekend periods.

Likewise, clients who prefer to eat the bulk of their daily food needs in the evening with their families, should be advised of the inefficiency of this pattern of eating, but not be forced to change, only to adapt their pattern of living. Advice on eating earlier, and avoiding carbohydrate elements in the evening meal, could be given.

30

Clients who have an active social life can be helped to cope with reduction plans without being a diet bore, or feeling that the diet places an unacceptable restraint on normal enjoyment. A client who feels that their diet deprives them in some way, is unlikely to follow it for any length of time. The diet has to be made to appear to add extra dimensions and variety to the daily food intake, rather than limiting the choice of ingredients.

How this is accomplished is a skilful aspect of the therapist's work, and requires her to have a sound knowledge of nutritional practice.

DIFFERENT FORMS OF DIET

The only sound, effective and safe diets to advise for long term weight loss and maintenance are those which re-educate the person's eating pattern overall. Fad diets, calorie-controlled foods, biscuits, liquid meals, etc., all play a part in helping the weight loss to be accomplished, but never establish a *normal* eating pattern. The re-adjustment of the food or energy intake has to be accomplished using ordinary food the person can live on for the rest of their life. No one could live on diet foods long term, so their use in establishing better patterns of eating is limited.

Recognizing the energy value of different foods is vital to the beauty therapist, as this helps her plan the diet for the client. The choice of diet can then be made, building in personal preferences, and allowing for problem areas to a small extent, such as a sweet tooth, social drinking, or a preference for fried food.

CARBOHYDRATE EXCLUSION DIETS

Carbohydrate exclusion diets can be provided by the carbohydrate unit diet (CU), which allow fats, dairy produce, etc., to be freely eaten along with proteins, green vegetables and selected fruits, but severely limits carbohydrates (starches, sugars, etc.). This diet allows for the social drinker, although the wasteful use of the allowed carbohydrate units on alcohol may leave the individual feeling deprived elsewhere in the diet, and a weight loss might not result. The carbohydrate exclusion diet can work very well in some instances, and the high fat content does avoid the feelings of hunger experienced on some diet plans. As it is difficult to eat excessive amounts of fat without some carbohydrate elements, the possibility of creating an imbalance of dietary elements is avoided with the CU diet. The actual units of carbohydrate permitted (the wasteful calories) can be adjusted if too much weight is being lost, or not enough. The ideal weight loss is 1½ kg (2 to 3 lb) a week, thus giving the skin time to re-adjust and not become slack.

CALORIE CONTROLLED DIETS

Calorie controlled diets still form the majority of sensible diet plans. They are a simple way of knowing that less food is being consumed and its value in energy terms, and when followed are bound to reduce the body weight.

High protein, low fat and low carbohydrate diets are probably the most popular of all diets, and allow for a great deal of flexibility and variety so keeping the client's interest. Getting the client to adhere to the diet is the problem in many cases — the diet works if only the individual follows it — but if they dislike what it offers, it will be rejected however sound in principle.

FOOD FOR A HEALTHY DIET

So use calorie controlled diets, but do not worry clients with the chore of adding up calories unless they appear to want to and it makes them feel personally involved with their plan. Simply give the client a set of pre-printed weekly diet sheets, modified to their individual needs (see pp. 34–5). These will provide a complete set of menus which can be alternated to fit changing circumstances. It will not make a great deal of difference if the heavy meal is in the evening rather than midday, which is nutritionally better, allowing the food to be used up more efficiently by the body, or if the midweek meals are lighter, and a little cheating takes place at the weekends. The scales will soon show if the overall trend is downwards, and if not, truthful discussion to pin-point the problem soon brings about a solution.

A sample client's brochure is shown on the next four pages.

32

HELP YOURSELF TO HEALTH AND BEAUTY

The clinic can help the slimmer in many ways, through dietary advice, exercise guidance, and beauty routines to tone and firm the figure whilst weight is being lost.

Many treatments are on offer to improve your figure — massage for relaxation — spas, saunas and steaming for fun and to prepare for vibratory, vacuum, muscle toning and cellulite routines; suntanning for a new image and special applications for breast and figure problems.

The therapist is expert at gaining results for her clients, helping their efforts, so have a plan specifically worked out for your figure needs — and create an attractive new image.

A RANGE OF TREATMENT

(a) Massage to relax and keep in top form

(b) Muscle contraction to tone and firm

(c) Galvanic body cellulite for fast results on this stubborn problem

DIET PLAN — LOW CARBOHYDRATE/MODERATE TO HIGH PROTEIN

Daily food plans for a week — which can be interchanged to suit tastes and social life. If a meal has to be miss

		MONDAY	TUESDAY
DAILY INTAKE OF FOOD ENERGY/CALORIES Female – Sedentary work — 　　1200-1500 C 　　– Moderately active — 　　1500-1700 C 　　– Very active/sports etc. — 　　1700-2200 C Males　– Sedentary work — 　　2000-2200 C 　　– Moderately active — 　　2200-2500 C 　　– Very active — 　　2500-3300 C If overweight — able to get a good pinch of flesh over the ribs or with visible weight problems — reduce daily intake by 500 C. — Consult your doctor if unsure of your health or severely overweight.	**BREAK-** **FAST**	Orange juice Cheese on 　toast (No butter)	Fresh fruit Scrambled 　egg and grilled tomato
PREFERRED FOODS — 　Proteins First Class　Meat/Fish 　　　　　　　　Eggs 　　　　　　　　Cheese 　　　Second Class　Nuts/Cereal 　　　　　Pulses 　　　　　Beans/Lentils Fruits and Vegetables 　All fruits fresh and unsweetened, apart from bananas. All green vegetables, cauliflower, carrots, peppers, peas, beans	**LUNCH**	Lean grilled chicken piece with salad No dressing or slimmer's salad dressing	Small steak with grilled tomato and peas or green beans
FOODS TO EAT MODERATELY OR AVOID Fats: butter, margarine, oil, salad dressing, fatty meat, bacon products, sausages Carbohydrates: sugar, starches, flour, sweets, sweetened drinks, pastries, crisps, fried chips **WAYS OF PREPARING FOOD** Eat as much fresh unprocessed food you can Grill/broil/bake your food — don't fry it or eat it with flour-based sauces, just thin gravy or natural juices Take your daily food intake from proteins, fruits and vegetables as much as possible, with moderate fats and carbohydrate only Many protein foods contain fats and carbohydrate as well — cheese, meat, milk If really hungry — eat more vegetables to fill up Use sugar substitutes in tea/coffee Don't restrict fluids, but drink water or unsweetened drinks — or milk (in moderation)	**DINNER**	Kebabs with onions, mushrooms Lean chunks of meat on skewer with onions and mushrooms — grilled (Marinate for a few hours before in small amount of wine) Serve with fresh tomatoes and celery	Pork fillet lean fillet of pork cooked in thin gravy flavoured with herbs and mushrooms Serve with green vegetables — beans or peas

stitute a slimmer's drink meal to avoid hunger or breaking the diet.

WEDNESDAY	THURSDAY	FRIDAY	SATURDAY	SUNDAY
Fruit juice Boiled egg or kipper/haddock Rye toast with scrape of margarine or butter	Plain omelette or with ham or cheese	Fruit/melon with ham or boiled egg with toast	Fresh fruit Poached egg on rye toast with scrape of margarine or butter	Fruit juice Kidney or lean bacon grilled, with tomato on rye toast (No butter)
Grilled trout or any other fish — cod — kingklip (not an oily fish) with tomato and peas or tinned tuna fish/salmon with salad (Drain any oil from can before using)	Ham salad with lots of tomatoes, celery, peppers etc. in the salad No dressing or slimmer's salad dressing	Cheese on toast or steak sandwich (No butter)	Spanish omlette — ham, tomato, mushrooms, with peas, beans, green vegetables or salad, or lean chops — lamb or pork with vegetables	Lean meat beef/chicken/ gammon/steak with green vegetables, carrots, peas Fruit or cheese on plain wafer biscuit
Steak and salad or gammon steak with thin slice of pineapple, sweetcorn (small portion), peas or beans, fresh tomato	Trout/other fish grilled with mushrooms Cheese can be added in moderation to fish to avoid dryness Serve with asparagus, boiled potato, beans	Liver/onion/ tomato bake Liver with onion rings, sliced tomato, sliced mush- rooms, baked in foil in the oven Herbs can be added for flavour Serve with vegetables or green beans	Roast or grilled chicken Remove all excess fat with kitchen paper Salad or green vegetables or ratatouille (peppers, tomato, celery mix)	Salad with plain omelette, ham or mushroom or tomato or tuna

POINTS TO HELP YOU SLIM

— Don't ever let unkind people deter you. Say to yourself, 'I want to be slim and attractive' — it could be jealousy that makes them tempt you.

— Never eat anything you don't feel like at that moment, whether on the diet plan or not. This is your body's appetite control starting to work — help it to get going.

— Give yourself the best of everything you can afford — make food a treat.

— Work towards the goal of reducing animal fats and refined sugar in your diet — for your health's sake as well as your figure's.

— Never force yourself to eat anything you do not like, substitute or have much less of something enjoyed even if its food value is higher. It's all food and feeds your body.

— If you don't like breakfast, have a meal replacement milk drink, or fruit and eat a little more mid-morning or lunch time. Try not to overload the evening meal — you do the least activity then.

— Start moving your body about — join the exercise class and have some fun. Don't forget the more you do, the more you can eat — the film star way of controlling weight.

— Use a body lotion all over after your shower each day to firm the skin and keep it supple as you start to lose weight — don't wait until you have lost it.

— If you don't like or want to eat protein — fish/meat — or it's beyond your budget, eat more vegetables, fruit, nuts and pulses (lentils, beans, etc.) but take care — it's easy to over-eat on these less effective proteins.

— Buy yourself a super new outfit — too small to get into — and keep trying it on to convince you you're winning, and how much better you'll look slimmer.

— Arrange your food attractively on smaller plates, and give as much variety as you can.

— Pin up a model picture you'd like to be like, near food sources — fridge, etc., just as a reminder of your slimming goal.

— If you feel like a binge — sit down and *dream* your way through eating all your favourites — then get up and have something else. If the temptation is too great, just get back on your diet as soon as you can — don't feel you have lost the cause.

THE ROLE OF EXERCISE

General exercise can be encouraged, even if just walking, gardening or enjoyable sports to increase the energy needs of the body. As clients get healthier and look trimmer, their will to exercise increases, and the therapist can turn this interest to advantage in the overall body improvement plan. Remember that any extra activity, however small, increases the body's call on its fuel reserves (its adipose tissue), and the accumulative effect of this can be seen over a period of time. Anybody who has been used to taking the car to work then starts walking instead, soon notices a difference both in weight, muscle tone and general vitality.

Exercise can be made to seem enjoyable to the client, especially as at present it is an 'in' thing to be seen jogging, doing exercise, and generally improving overall fitness. So encouraging the client to participate should not be too difficult.

It is important to remember that all activity is exercise, including domestic chores, social events, dancing, swimming and sports of all kinds. Clients tend to associate 'exercise' with boring repetitive routines, which they feel foolish performing. To overcome this problem, group exercise sessions, movement and dance, or yoga may be suggested, and the client encouraged to pick the area which appeals to them personally.

DANCE IS VERY MUCH THE 'IN' EXERCISE

Some clients prefer very strenuous workouts, and like pushing themselves to their limits. Others prefer to exercise with a variety of apparatus, and like to work against their previous best efforts in terms of repetitions and power. Many clients like to exercise specifically, so that every exercise really counts, and accomplish muscular co-ordination on independent areas of the body. Figure shaping or body building requires this detailed and dedicated approach if full success is to be achieved.

Probably the vast majority of clients like to combine the best elements of many different forms of exercise. Walking and general active (isotonic) exercise for mobility and respiratory improvement; concentrated exercise of the isotonic or isometric type (static contractions) for specific toning effects, and resistance exercises where an increase in muscle bulk is desired.

For further information on exercise routines, see *Body Treatments and Dietetics for the Beauty Therapist,* by Ann Gallant.

4

Massage techniques

The touch of the human hand — as in massage — can never be replaced! Its form and technique is forever growing, even though some of the scientific avenues of rationalization about its effects have not been fully understood or explored. The para-medical beauty therapist is slowly gathering momentum as a means to preventive medicine, and the good relationship between beauty therapists and the medical profession is ever increasing.

The word 'massage' describes the manipulation of soft tissues of the body to stimulate the nervous and muscular systems and the local and general circulation of the blood and lymph. There are various methods of doing this to create a range of different effects, some relaxing, some invigorating.

Manual techniques range from the standard or general massage routine, which is applied to the whole body, to specialized techniques such as nerve point or connective tissue massage for specific areas and conditions. The general body massage is based on established classifications of basic movements, and these remain the basis for various forms of manual massage application. Whatever the type of massage, they all rely on a correctly applied classic technique altered and adapted to suit the personal requirements of the client.

The three main established massage classifications are *effleurage* (a stroking movement), *petrissage* (a kneading manipulation), and *tapotement* (a percussion or beating effect). These movements are used in varying combinations to produce a range of effects of both physical and psychological benefit to the client. So the manner in which the movements are applied is more important than the actual sequence or routine of massage chosen, as long as some basic principles are adhered to. In addition to the basic movements there are vibrations which are used for special effects, and concentrated pressure movements, such as used in connective tissue massage, aromatherapy and acupressure massage.

MASSAGE AND HEAT

(a) Massage is used to hasten elimination using petrissage, compression movements, initially working gently to avoid discomfort on tense muscle areas

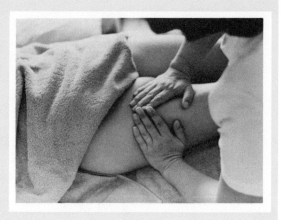

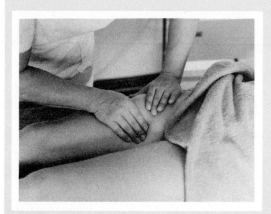

(b) Deep kneading is used firmly and deeply to improve biological functioning in the area, and speed vascular and lymphatic circulation

(c) Effleurage, stroking movements, are used to link strokes and relieve any discomfort or spasm in the muscles

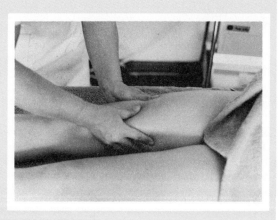

DEVELOPING TECHNIQUE IN MANUAL MASSAGE

All the more specialized forms of massage require an attentive approach, and skill and experience on the part of the therapist. They also need strength to apply correctly, and control to ensure no harmful effects are produced. Most massage routines, however, even for special purposes, are based on the classic massage movements, so it is essential to build skills in basic massage routines before progressing to advanced techniques. In this way the correct body posture, rate and rhythm of strokes and pressure adjustment become established, while strength, stamina, and control develop slowly.

Without these essential techniques becoming established, the therapist would be unable to progress to specialized routines and achieve the desired effects. Also, without a thoughtful awareness of the state of the body, the need for the more specialized massage applications would not be apparent. Connective tissue massage and aromatherapy techniques both rely heavily on the therapist's assessment of the client's physical and psychological state. The results obtained are directly related to her judgement and choice of massage strokes, essential oils if used, pressure positions, etc., so a deep knowledge of the body is essential. This is why it is impossible to 'teach' aromatherapy for example, as it relies so heavily on personal ability and judgement of the individual client's need. All that is possible is to learn the component elements, effects of different movements, the actions and effects of individual oils, etc., and then develop the technique gradually by using the methods and building knowledge of the reactions achieved. Once basic skills are established, the therapist is then able to acquire new methods of treatment very easily, adding them to her treatment range to provide variety to maintain client interest.

There are many different types of massage that the therapist should be able to offer, or at least be aware of, the most popular being relaxation massage, which is often termed a general massage. The general massage often contains too many stimulatory movements to be truly relaxing, although the client will feel regenerated by the experience.

RELAXATION MASSAGE

This type of massage is chosen for its relief of nervous tension effects, and needs to be applied by a caring and skilled therapist, if it is to be successful. It is comprised mainly of effleurage strokes, applied rhythmically with even pressure, and an even rate of movements, to accomplish a general release of mental and physical tensions. Maximum benefit is gained when the massage

follows some form of heat therapy, such as a sauna or steam bath or a session under a heat lamp. This relaxes contracted muscles in preparation for the manual application.

The restful, warm atmosphere relaxes muscles, and a professional but sympathetic approach to the client will ensure the most satisfactory results. There is a growing demand for this form of massage, mainly because of the increasing stresses of daily life. It is a form of massage indicated where a client is highly strung, nervous or tense, or where fatigue and depression are causing muscular pain and a general feeling of lassitude. All traumatic elements are excluded from the massage sequence. The client's relaxation is maintained throughout the routine and all areas of the body are massaged in a systematic manner. The routine follows a pattern of effleurage stroking movements followed by petrissage compression, applied slowly and rhythmically. These deeper movements are linked and concluded by superficial effleurage on each section of the body before proceeding to the next body area. Each part of the body should be kept warm during the treatment, and wrapped snugly to retain the warmth after massage in the area has been completed. The massage may commence on the back area, if this is an area of special tension, so relieving the contracted nature of the muscle fibres in that area first, and thus allowing the client to benefit more fully from the following routine. The client should feel cherished and comforted by the relaxation massage routine, and may well fall asleep during its application. If space is available, as in hydrotherapy, for the client to be left to sleep quietly for an hour or so after the treatment, this increases the overall benefit of the massage. The ideal period of time for this massage is 45 minutes to 1 hour for the client to gain maximum benefit from the routine.

TONING MASSAGE

Toning or sports massage creates a totally different physical effect on the various body systems, stimulating them into greater activity while improving muscular tone by relaxation and improvement of general body functions.

It requires a more active routine, with petrissage and tapotement movements forming the basis of the massage routine. Specific areas of the body can be treated where muscular tension is most evident — for example the back, or in the site of an old injury if the client is an athlete. Or a general massage can be given with the emphasis being placed on the larger muscle groups and the extremities being excluded or dealt with very superficially.

The routine can be adapted to individual needs and will depend on the purpose of the application. General body toning, relief of

muscular tension in the legs, shoulders, arms or upper back are all conditions where a more vigorous massage sequence would be indicated.

Athletes, sportsmen and the younger or physically fit clients of all age groups benefit most from this form of manual maintenance, which keeps them in firm muscular condition and reduces the possibility of adipose deposits accumulating. The routine for a toning massage makes it a tiring routine to perform for the therapist, and so vibratory massage is often introduced to save operator fatigue. This reduces the overall treatment time, but is naturally less personal and will not be accepted by all clients. The normal timing of the toning massage would be 30 to 45 minutes, but naturally this can be altered according to the client's need, and the linked treatments with which the massage is associated such as saunas, steam baths, or hydrotherapy. A really fit person will have a greater capacity for treatment, and may be able to take and enjoy a treatment combination which would exhaust a less highly-toned individual. So with the therapist's professional guidance, the clients can decide what is beneficial to them.

AROMATHERAPY TREATMENT

Aromatherapy is the use of essential oils in therapeutic and cosmetology treatments, applied in association with specialized manual massage routines. Essential oils are the vital elements of plants, and are extracted from either the roots, stalks, flowers or fruits of the plant, and are considered to be vegetable hormones. The specialized aromatherapy massage has to be devised individually for the client, and can be made to accomplish many different effects, the best known being its relaxation benefits. It can be devised to stimulate the circulation, calm the nervous system, help with insomnia, and as a means to relieve depression. These effects are produced by blending the essential oils, which are then used within the massage, and at home to maintain the overall effect.

The treatments follow a basic pattern which is adapted to suit each client's individual need, and although the massage technique incorporates certain familiar movements, it cannot be compared with a standard massage system. It works on the pressure points and nerve endings which control so much of the action and tensions of the body.

It also differs from the more traditional forms of body therapy massage by combining work on both the face and body. Aromatherapy has a very special place in the therapist's range of skills, but it does require special training to gain the necessary knowledge of the oils and their effects, and experience of the actual massage and its methods of application.

The aromatherapy routine is a full one hour sequence, which allows the treatment to be really effective. The atmosphere in which the treatment is completed, and the sympathetic approach of the therapist are vital points for the success of the routine. Aromatherapy is really for the skilled massage therapist to perform, and should be studied when sufficient expertise in basic massage techniques has become established. Without a sound knowledge of the body, and insight into the client's inner tensions, the therapist would be unable to form a valued judgement on individual clients' needs, and so would be unlikely to give a beneficial treatment. There is also the danger that with inexperience the therapist could perform a harmful treatment, particularly as the effects of the essential oils can be very strong.

CONNECTIVE TISSUE MASSAGE

Connective tissue massage stimulates certain physiological responses which take place in the connective layer of the body. Connective tissue is widely distributed around the body, weaving itself like a thread through all the structures. Its function is to provide a framework of support for important organs while simultaneously reinforcing the blood vessels, nerves, bones, muscles, lymphatics and developing tissue spaces. It forms the superficial and deep fascia; the former blending with the skin and the latter concerned with muscles and bony attachments.

This kind of connective tissue is known as the *loose form* and it is with this that connective tissue massage (CTM) is concerned. One of the cells which make up the tissue is called the *mast cell*, which liberates histamine and heparin. The connective tissue massage technique produces the triple response which relies on histamine being released from the mast cells.

The axon reflex, is basically responsible for the *triple response* which comprises the red streak, a generalized flush and a white wheal if the skin is stroked firmly with controlled pressure using the middle finger supported by the ring finger.

This stroke technique uses different lengths of strokes, long and short, and altering pressure sensations to create a range of effects — most concerned with improving the function of an area, or increasing the peripheral circulation. Diagnosis and choice of movements is based on a visual and manual examination of the body, first the back, with the client in a sitting position, then manually with the client prone. Any deviations from the normal condition of the back, or other areas of the body can then be assessed, and this is where the real skill of the treatment lies. Areas of tension, swelling, tenderness, etc., can be seen or felt, or both, and these help to determine the pattern of the treatment and the area of concentration.

44

Some of the effects of CTM include circulatory and digestive improvement, relaxation of tension and its effects, improved skin function and increased effects on sweat glands. It can also be used as a sleep inducer for insomnia. Many connective tissue movements are used within aromatherapy, in combination with essential oils.

Connective tissue massage will produce both local and general effects, and is a highly specialized form of therapy requiring special training and knowledge. The general effects of this massage stimulate the peripheral circulation and an extensive treatment could be dangerous, due to the changes occurring in the blood pressure. In most cases with a beauty therapy situation, limited but concentrated applications of connective tissue massage will be used for special effects rather than it being extensively applied.

5

Heat therapy, hydrotherapy and linked treatments

One of the essential elements in providing a total body service is to have some method of pre-heating the body available, either in the form of lamps, water baths, vapour or dry heat systems, such as steam baths or saunas. Which system will depend on the space available, the initial cost of purchase, and any planning or health restrictions in force, rather than personal choice in many cases. The novelty value of attracting new clients is another factor to consider when choosing a system of pre-heating to offer. Clients who come to try a form of heating routine — just to experience the sensation and enjoy themselves — can often be converted into regular clients, if approached sympathetically. The important thing is to get the client to attend in the first instance, so that the therapist has the opportunity to help them with any figure problem they may have. Treatments like saunas, hydrotherapy units, plunge pools, etc., can do this, as they are seen as enjoyable, and demand little from the client.

The actual value to the client when heat therapy treatments are added to the clinic's treatment range is enormous, as beneficial effects are gained at every stage of the routine. By using pre-heating measures on the client, tense muscle fibres are relaxed, contracted muscles are relieved through the effects of the warmth, and the massage or electrical application becomes easier to apply and more comfortable for the client.

When the body is warm and the tissues saturated with moisture, as after a hydrotherapy or steam bath session, muscle contractions are initiated at a much lower level due to the decrease in skin resistance, and because the tissues act as an excellent conductor to the faradic-type currents. So client comfort is improved, and the treatment is more effective and results are obtained more quickly. This leads directly to client satisfaction, which is always good for business.

Treatments which leave the surface tissues full of moisture in the epidermal layers, are excellent preparation for electrical therapy which requires currents to pass through the skin with the minimum resistance. These include treatments such as faradism, interferential routines, and galvanism for 'cellulite'. So steam baths, hydrotherapy, or even impulse showers are excellent for pre-heating in this instance.

Dry heat treatments such as saunas (for general application) or lamps (for localized areas), act in much the same way, improving the circulation, increasing the temperature and colour of the surface tissues, as the body attempts to lose heat. So the muscles and tissues are receptive to manual and electrical therapy, such as manual and vibratory massage, vacuum routines, etc. Dry heat treatments are also an effective pre-heating sequence to muscle contraction as well, as the muscles are relaxed, but the reduction in skin resistance and improved conductivity of the tissues are not so apparent.

If a careful record of the client's individual treatments is kept, it is possible to assess which pre-heating treatment was most effective in terms of reduced intensities of current to achieve good results, and improved client comfort. With muscle contraction — if treatments are recorded which show the current intensity needed to overcome skin resistance and initiate a good muscular response, first on a dry, normal temperature skin, then on a warm, moist skin on a relaxed client — the differences point out the advantages of pre-heating very clearly.

CLIENT COMFORT

Probably the greatest advantage of pre-heating is the improvement in client comfort, particularly with electrical therapy, where the client can be anxious, unsure of the sensation to be experienced, and perhaps nervous of the effects of the treatment. If discomfort is reduced, the client can have a much more effective routine applied, and is not so restricted by the sensation experienced, which in many cases limits the value of the application. This is a special problem with the older client, who is less willing to try electrical treatments anyway. Muscle contraction and vacuum massage routines are two prime examples of where the client comfort, or lack of comfort, determines the length of the actual application, and the results that can be obtained.

DIFFERENT FORMS OF HEAT THERAPY

The forms of heating available fall into several main areas, which achieve rather similar effects. There are the moist heat routines, such as steaming, either in the form of steam rooms, or more

commonly these days, steam bath cabinets. Then there are the dry heat routines such as saunas, and lamps using radiant heat and infra-red. Lastly the hydrotherapy units, which take many forms including spa-baths, the underwater pressure massage, using pulsed air, and the cabinets which combine water therapy with oxygen baths, where the client is alternately sprayed with hot and cold water jets.

SAUNA BATHS

The sauna routine is very popular, particularly in countries where there is a lack of natural warmth such as the United Kingdom. As clients have not been brought up with saunas as part of their daily life they have to become accustomed to the heat levels slowly, otherwise accidents might occur caused by fainting or dizziness.

Sauna cabinets capable of seating 4 to 5 people are adequate for most small clinic purposes. Larger units are uneconomic to operate unless they can be fully booked at most times. Heating times range from ½ to 1 hour for most 6 to 9 kilowatt stoves

A SAUNA

48

before the sauna has reached an operating temperature. The sauna has advantages and disadvantages in clinic use. The advantages are that people find it enjoyable, it is low on supervision and maintenance, and can be very profitable if promoted by staff in both a pre-heating and pure enjoyment capacity.

The disadvantages are that clients' individual temperatures cannot be controlled, so that the overall set heat of the sauna will not suit all the clients within it. The only method of adjustment being to sit closer or further away from the source of heat (the stove), once an overall sauna temperature is set. Another factor is the cost of running the sauna, which can be very high in relation to profit, if the sauna is not kept booked fairly consistently.

As with all pre-heating treatments, these minor problems can be overcome by promoting treatments well, and ensuring staff are really aware of the special advantages of pre-heating prior to therapy routines wherever possible. If staff are not convinced of the value of the sauna applications, they will not promote them and the service will run at a loss.

The actual effects of the sauna are to raise body temperature, increase surface blood pressure, causing a change in colour, warmth of the skin, etc. Internal blood pressure drops, and as the head is involved in this routine, this could result in sensations of faintness, giddiness, etc. So first-time sauna users should be watched very closely, and their treatments monitored as to time, level of heat, showering and rest periods, etc., to avoid mishaps occurring.

In the sauna the body becomes warm, and as the client relaxes, muscular tension is released, and the products of fatigue, stress and tension, such as lactic acid accumulations in the muscles are dispersed. The effect is of course accelerated by the subsequent massage which clients should be encouraged to have for full benefit.

After a few minutes the body begins to sweat, and the skin is cleansed, and a fluid loss results. If clients find it difficult to perspire, they can be advised to shower prior to entering the sauna, which solves the problem in most cases. The routine of alternating the sauna with showers can be adjusted for individual clients. If a client enjoys breaking the routine by showering, resting, etc., this is acceptable, but not essential to gain benefit from the routine. It is also very stimulating, and should not be advised until the client's capacity for the sauna treatment is known. Likewise cold showers are not mandatory, and cool showers less of a shock to the system. Many clients simply enjoy being in the sauna at a low temperature, showering with warm water, and then having a pleasant relaxing massage. The whole sauna routine need take only ½ hour, and if it is to be followed by massage treatment, will take 1¼ to 1½ hours in total. If treatment does not follow the sauna the client must be

advised to rest until the body resumes its normal temperature, ½ hour at least. So resting facilities are a necessity, one of the reasons why saunas can be a more difficult treatment to offer initially, as the total treatment sequence requires more space.

If clients wish to take longer over their saunas, they can be advised to attend earlier, so they may take as long as they like over the routine, and still be ready when the therapist is booked to treat them.

STEAM BATHS

Steam baths provide a controllable and simple means of heating the body, which has the advantage that the head is left free. This is useful where the client has delicate skin or existing capillary damage on the face.

The blood pressure of the body becomes lower internally, and higher on the skin's surface, and there is an overall increase in the pulse rate. There is a rise in body temperature, producing colour and heat on the skin's surface, and resulting in sweating. This produces a small fluid loss in the body. Clients find it easy to perspire, as their skins are covered with moisture from the vapour provided from the water heating in the steam baths' tanks.

The whole mechanism of the steam bath unit is simple and the maintenance is low, particularly with the fibreglass baths. The effects on the body are excellent for pre-heating prior to manual

A STEAM
BATH

and electrical therapy, or as a treatment in its own right for relieving stiffness in the muscles, tension or fatigue. Skin cleansing effects are also good, as the skin's stratum corneum is softened, and dead skin can be desquamated (shed), rubbed away and rinsed off in the shower. This leaves the skin very clean, finely textured, and less liable to skin blemishes, etc.

Weight lost through the fluid loss of the sequence is soon readjusted by the body, so this factor of treatment should not be stressed to clients. As a means of maintaining a weight loss to keep the body weight balanced it is very useful, just as one light diet day would be on a maintenance diet programme. Fluid loss is not enough to accomplish weight loss on its own, so should not be promoted in this way, otherwise clients expect the wrong benefit from the application. Relaxation and preparation for further treatment are the main advantages of heat therapy, not weight loss. Application times of 15 to 20 minutes are normally sufficient for most people, and clients should be advised against long steam bath sessions.

HEAT LAMPS

Heat lamps are a simple and effective low-cost method of heating the body, and they are useful where the more generalized body heating routines are inappropriate. This may be due to space or planning restrictions. The client may be contra-indicated to general body heating but able to accept localized heat applications.

Infra-red and radiant heat lamps are used, either in the form of individual lamps, or as overhead solaria. Application need only be for a few minutes before the massage or vacuum treatment is given. The lamp may also be left in position during the treatment, or after its conclusion to maximize the effects. Combined treatments such as massage of the upper trapezius muscles, with infrared ray applications, show how effective this approach can be.

Radiant heat creates a more immediate response on the skin's surface, but because it is a form of visible light, causes more surface irritation. This can halt the treatment prematurely before the desired relaxation effects are achieved. For this reason infrared is more commonly chosen for combination with massage, as its

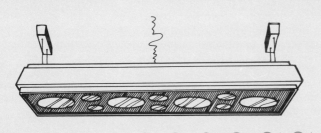

A MULTIPLE
HEAT LAMP

51

TWIN HEADED
TREATMENT LAMP
(ULTRA-VIOLET AND
INFRA-RED)

effects are slower, but being more acceptable to the body (being invisible heat) can be used for longer periods without irritation, and without mottled skin occurring.

Both infra-red and radiant heat are forms of heat which achieve their circulatory effects by a counter irritation effect. The surface capillaries dilate, and heat is produced which the body attempts to lose from its surface. Deeper placed blood vessels respond to this need for blood at the skin's surface, and in turn dilate and provide a greater interchange of vascular fluid. This interchange of blood and nutrients helps to disperse toxic elements in the surface tissues, and within the muscle fibres, such as lactic acid which might be causing muscular pain, tiredness, etc. Fibrous thickenings which may be present as a result of the muscular tension can also be reduced or dispersed in time.

So there are many advantages to using lamps as a form of treatment, quite apart from their ability to heat the area and make it more ready and able to benefit from the subsequent treatment.

HYDROTHERAPY, AIR BATHS, JACUZZIS

A popular system of treatment, the hydrotherapy units come in a variety of forms, the best known being the pulsed air bath, whirlpool or jacuzzi. A complete bath unit is installed, which provides for pulsed underwater massage and acts as a stimulatory treatment for the client. Hydrotherapy is normally used as a treatment on its own, rather than as a combined routine, as its effects on the body can be rather exhausting as well as relaxing. The air bath is used for a variety of conditions, toning, relaxation, within reduction programmes, and when of short duration can be used as a preparation for massage or electrical routines.

A SPA BATH

The resistance the body provides to the air pressure can be very tiring if not controlled well, so it is worth beginning with short treatment periods if the client is not to feel unduly fatigued. The air pressure may be directed from the base of the bath, or the sides, or may be applied as an air or water jet held under the water by the therapist, and directed towards the client. Baths such as the whirlpool or jacuzzi naturally require the least staff involvement, as once settled, the client can be left for 15 to 20 minutes according to their tolerance. The pressure of the jets can be adjusted to suit an individual client in the smaller baths, while in the larger units the clients can simply remove themselves from the bath when they need to rest.

Herbal essences and seaweed extracts can be added to the water to increase the enjoyment and effect of the routine. Bubble oils may be used to add to the luxury of the routine, but must be especially formulated for professional use, otherwise they will clog up the air jets of the bath. After the routine, the clients shower if they wish, and then rest, or have a restful application such as facial therapy, manicure, pedicure, or hairstyling.

The differences in the individual systems of pre-heating routines have been considered briefly. As independent treatments, the effects of the varied forms of heat therapy differ considerably and these effects must be studied if the treatment applied is to suit the client and not exhaust them physically. The contra-indications to each treatment must also be known.

6

Figure diagnosis

When assessing the figure for treatment purposes it is important to remember that the client is an individual whose body has undergone change, the results of which are likely to be evident if one is able to read the signs. Factors such as age, health, body-type, tendency to adipose deposits, and the medical background of the client are vital signposts for suggesting the safest method of treatment.

These signs also provide guidance as to what is likely to be possible within the figure improvement plan, and how quickly the improvement may be achieved. Many of the faults of the body are postural in origin, and it is important to check the client's standing and moving posture very carefully, as any faults spotted here, which can be corrected by exercise, will improve the overall results obtained dramatically. All postural defects are skeletal in origin, and directly linked with the muscular tone and strength, and extensibility of the muscle fibres, which support the bones and permit movement to occur. The body's muscular tone and actual adipose deposits must also be assessed, as these may point to different methods of treatment being advisable. Muscular weakness needs a totally different approach when planning a programme, than simple subcutaneous fat problems. Fat can be lost by diet, or by increasing the body's energy output; muscular weakness has to be rectified slowly, and is a more difficult problem.

When an initial assessment is completed by the therapist it is advisable to record all the factors visible, whether postural, muscular, or associated with adipose deposits. There is no need in a therapy situation to have separate records relating to postural defects, it simply makes the task unwieldy. If the client is watched when moving naturally, the general posture and range of movement can be judged, which helps in the diagnosis. In this way an overall picture is gained, which can be added to both through conversation, and subsequent treatment of the body, perhaps through manual massage. A static assessment of the figure does not provide the whole picture, but it is a starting point to which can be added muscular knowledge, when the client is given simple mobility exercises to perform. These will test their muscular ability, and the tension or shortening of the muscle fibres that is present. It will also indicate what improvement can be expected.

(a)

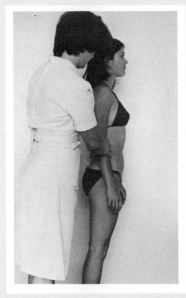

(a), (b) Check the client's posture so that they can relate to how they should feel and move when their muscles are strong and holding them firmly

(b)

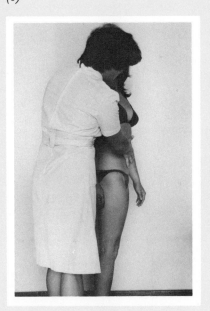

(c) Encourage the client's exercise efforts, using isometric exercise initially if the muscles are weak

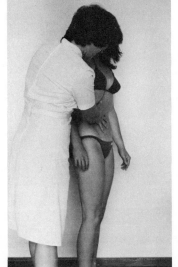

GENERAL BODY ASSESSMENT

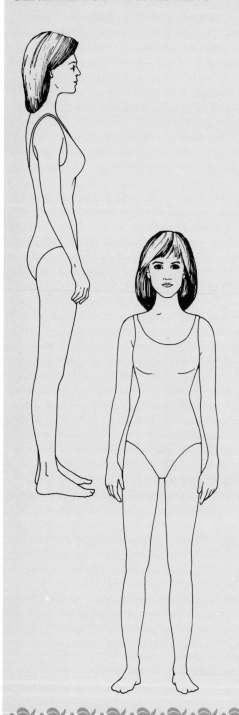

Figure faults — check list

— *Head tilt*
— *High shoulders*
— *Scapula abduction*
— *Dowager's hump*
— *Adipose deposits on the biceps/triceps muscles*
— *Poor muscle tone on the triceps muscles*
— *Rib cage/breasts*
— *Back: flat back*
        round back
        scoliosis
        kyphosis
— *Waist*
— *Abdomen: abdominal bulge*
— *Buttocks*
— *Pelvic tilt*
— *Legs: muscular tone*
        adipose deposits
        cellulite
        knock knees
        bow legs
        hyper-extended legs
— *Feet: flat feet*

MUSCLES CONCERNED WITH ERECT POSTURE

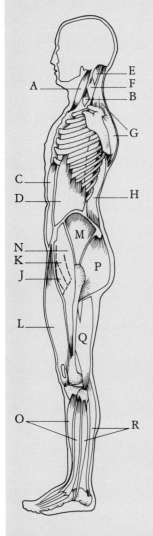

Muscles of the trunk

(i) Anterior:
A   *Sternomastoid*
B   *Longus colli*
C   *Rectus abdominis*
D   *Oblique muscles of the abdomen*

(ii) Posterior:
E   *Splenius capitis*
F   *Splenius colli*
G   *Trapezius*
H   *Lower part of long spinal muscles*

Muscles of the lower limb

(i) Anterior:
J   *Psoas*
K   *Iliacus*
L   *Quadriceps*
M   *Gluteus medius and minimus*
N   *Tensor fasciae latae*
O   *Long extensors of toes and the anterior tibial muscle*

(ii) Posterior:
P   *Gluteus maximus*
Q   *Hamstring muscles*
R   *Long flexors of toes, the calf and posterior tibial muscle*

SUMMARY OF MUSCLE ACTIONS

Muscles which co-operate to produce movement at joints in order of importance:

VERTEBRAL COLUMN
CERVICAL

Flexion: sternomastoids, longus colli and scaleni (scalenus anticus, medius, posticus).

Extension: splenii capitis, splenii colli, trapezius and upper part of erector spinae.

Lateral flexion: sternomastoids, scaleni, levator scapulae, trapezius and upper part of erector spinae, all of one side.

Rotation: sternomastoid of one side, small rotators of the cervical part of the vertebral column and upper part of erector spinae.

DORSAL AND LUMBAR

Flexion: rectus abdominis, obliques and psoas and iliacus of both sides. (Gravity performs most of this action in the erect position.)

Extension: erector spinae, latissimus dorsi and trapezius of both sides can assist when shoulder is fixed.

Lateral flexion: obliques, rectus abdominis, spinal muscles, latissimus dorsi, quadratus lumborum and psoas, all of one side.

Rotation: external oblique of one side with the internal oblique of the opposite side assisted by erector spinae and short spinal muscles.

RESPIRATION

Quiet: diaphragm, rectus abdominis, oblique and transversalis intercostals.

Deep: sternomastoid, scaleni, pectorals, latissimus dorsi and quadratus lumborum of both sides.

SHOULDER GIRDLE
SCAPULA

Forward: pushing, thrusting and especially reaching movements — serratus anterior and pectoralis minor.

Backward: bracing shoulders, trapezius and rhomboids.

Elevation: shrugging the shoulders, trapezius and levator scapulae.

Depression: latissimus dorsi and lower fibres of the trapezius.

SHOULDER JOINT

Flexion: pectoralis major, anterior fibres of the deltoid, biceps and brachialis.

Extension: posterior fibres of the deltoid, latissimus dorsi, triceps, and teres major.

Abduction: supraspinatus and deltoid to 90% — further elevation by rotation of scapula on chest wall, principally by trapezius.

Adduction: pectoralis major, latissimus dorsi, infra-spinatus, teres major and minor, sub-scapularis and long head of the triceps.

58

Medial rotation: pectoralis major, deltoid (anterior) and latissimus dorsi, teres major.

Lateral rotation: infraspinatus, deltoid (posterior) and teres minor.

ELBOW

Flexion: biceps, brachialis and flexor group of forearm muscles.

Extension: triceps and anconeus.

FOREARM

Pronation: pronator teres and pronator guadratus.

Supination: supinator assisted by biceps.

HIP JOINT

Flexion: psoas, iliacus, rectus femoris, sartorius, and adductors in early stage.

Extension: gluteus maximus, biceps femoris, semimembranosus, semitendinosus (hamstrings) bending controlled by hamstrings.

Abduction: gluteus maximus active when the thigh is extended against resistance, as in rising from bending or sitting position, or when walking upstairs.

Abduction: gluteus medius and minimus assisted by sartorius and tensor fasciae latae.

Adduction: adductors longus, brevis and magnus, assisted by pectineus and gracilis (as in riding) wider range when thigh is flexed.

Medial rotation: gluteus medius and minimus, tensor fasciae latae, psoas.

Lateral rotation: small muscles arising from the hip bone and inserted into the back of the upper end of the femur, assisted by gluteus maximus and sartorius.

KNEE JOINT

Flexion: biceps femoris, semimembranosus, semitendinosus, sartorius, and gastrocnemius when the foot is on the ground.

Extension: quadriceps.

ANKLE JOINT

Dorsiflexion: tibialis anterior assisted by extensor digitorum longus, extensor hallucis longus (long extensors of the toes) and peroneus tertius.

Plantarflexion: gastrocnemius, soleus, assisted by posterior tibial muscle and long flexors of the toes.

FOOT	supports weight of the body in standing or progression, and to act as lever to propel body forwards in walking, running or jumping.
ARCHES Longitudinal:	peroneus longus which passes beneath the sole. Tibialis anterior from the front and tibialis posterior from the back of the leg forming a double sling or stirrup to support the arches of the foot. Long flexors of the toes, intrinsic muscles of the foot.
Inversion:	posterior and anterior tibial muscles.
Eversion:	peroneus longus and peroneus brevis.

PELVIC TILT

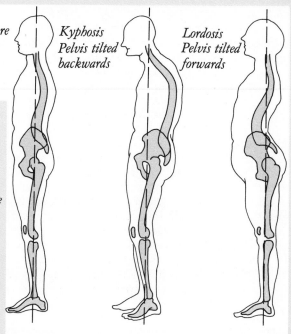

Good posture Pelvic tilt correct

Kyphosis Pelvis tilted backwards

Lordosis Pelvis tilted forwards

The pelvis is held on the femoral heads tilted at an angle of 55° to 65°. If pelvic tilt is correct, the pubic symphysis and the anterior superior iliac spines are in the same plane

To measure pelvic tilt draw an imaginary line through the lumbosacral joint and the pubic symphysis. Draw a line horizontal to this and the angle of tilt where they meet

SCOLIOSIS

A Single C-shaped curve
B Primary curve
C Compensatory curve

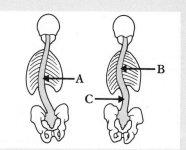

60

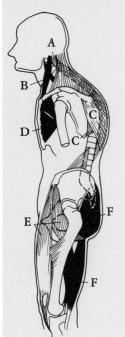

Diagram showing the lengthened muscles (shaded) and the shortened antagonists (black) associated with round back and round shoulders

A *Extensors of neck and upper part of the back*
B *Flexors of the neck*
C *Muscles connecting the scapula to vertebrae*
D *Pectorals*
E *Flexors of the hip*
F *Extensors of the hip*

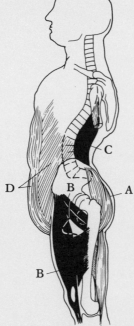

Diagram showing the lengthened muscles (shaded) and the shortened antagonists (black) associated with hollow back

A *Extensors of the hip*
B *Flexors of the hip*
C *Lower portion of long spinal muscles*
D *Muscles of the abdominal wall*

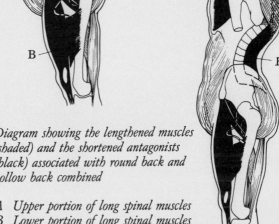

Diagram showing the lengthened muscles (shaded) and the shortened antagonists (black) associated with round back and hollow back combined

A *Upper portion of long spinal muscles*
B *Lower portion of long spinal muscles*

LEVERS

First order:

The fulcrum, F, is between the weight, W, and the power, P. The example shows F is the joint between the atlas and the skull; W is the weight of the skull and P is the power exerted by the muscles which draw the head downwards

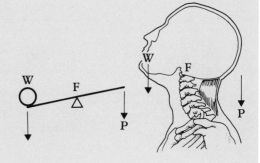

Second order:

The weight, W, is between the fulcrum, F, and the power, P. The action of the calf muscles raising the body on the toes illustrates this in the body (mechanical advantage)

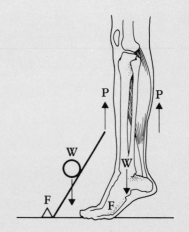

Third order:

The power, P, is between the fulcrum, F, and the weight, W. Flexion of the elbow (mechanical disadvantage)

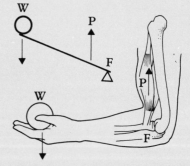

7

Electrical frequencies in beauty therapy

One of the areas of beauty least understood by therapists, and which causes the most hesitation and anxiety in its use is the application of electrical currents in clinic treatments. If the electrical frequencies available to the therapist are considered, the effect they have on the body can be clearly seen, and it becomes obvious how these can be put to good use in beauty therapy practice.

Relatively new in terms of their general application in therapy, electrical treatments have an important contribution to make to the results obtainable in treatment. If well presented and used with confidence, electrical therapy soon gains client acceptance, and will produce effects which cannot be produced manually or cosmetically. It will also reinforce and speed the client's efforts, bringing encouraging results more quickly to spur on individual home programmes.

So electrical frequencies used either independently or in a treatment programme alongside manual, cosmetic or exercise aspects, speed results, and can produce special effects unobtainable by any other method of treatment, and work to reinforce the client's efforts.

A range of frequencies are available to the qualified therapist, capable of producing very varied effects for face and body treatments. If the *effects* of the different types or levels of frequency are understood in terms of being general or specific, then conditions which would benefit from these effects quickly come to mind, and the frequency can be applied to good effect. Electrical frequencies used in beauty therapy are normally termed high, medium, and low frequency, most of which fall within a certain band or area of oscillation or alternating wave frequency. They all have distinctive wave patterns which indicate the form of the frequency and the sensation the client will experience. Many different systems of treatment operate on these frequencies, including high frequency, short wave diathermy epilation, interferential and faradic-type muscle contraction applications.

The main purpose of using electrical current is to stimulate or speed natural body processes. As the body has its own natural electrical energy, electrical frequencies can be used to good effect to encourage the body to work to full capacity and regain or maintain vitality and strength.

All the processes occurring in the body naturally are accompanied by small electrical currents generated by the individual cells. This activity can be enhanced by careful choice and use of electrical therapy to bring the body to correct functioning.

The forms of current that the therapist is permitted to apply include direct current, and low-frequency, medium-frequency and high-frequency currents. The manner in which she is permitted to apply the currents must fall within accepted beauty therapy practice, and on no account must they be used for electro-medical purposes unless the therapist also holds the relevant medical or para-medical qualification necessary.

Although the currents that the therapist uses are similar or indeed identical to those used within physiotherapy, their application has a different purpose. Therapists use electrical currents to maintain health, while the physiotherapist uses them to regain health and function. The therapist's role is preventive, and linked with health maintenance, while the physiotherapist's is remedial, helping the body and the person back to health.

COMPARISON OF FREQUENCIES

If the electrical frequencies available to the therapist can be thought of as a scale — starting from high to low — their effects can be clearly understood.

High frequencies oscillate so fast they cannot cause muscle contraction, but create vascular stimulation, warmth, relaxation and relief from stress. They can also be drying, cause chemical effects or be destructive when used specifically. In some cases the client acts to complete the circuit and allow flow transmission of the current, in other instances this is unnecessary as the electrodes are of single polarity. In all cases the amount of voltage used is minimal, and the current flows superficially under the skin, or is dissipated into the surface tissues.

Medium to low frequencies allow muscular and biological activity to take place, and when correctly placed according to the system used, produce clear comfortable contractions and visible muscular activity. Only the area directly concerned with the application is involved in the muscular activity, so the effect is localized. Muscle contraction does not produce any chemical effects, but like natural exercise produces lactic acid in the muscles, increases vascular flow locally and increases the skin temperature.

Direct current — such as galvanic

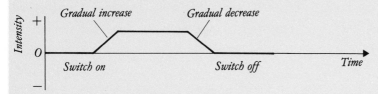

High frequency

Medium frequency — interferential

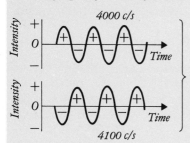
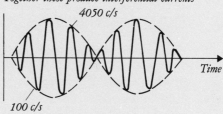

Low frequency — impulse, faradic, muscle contraction

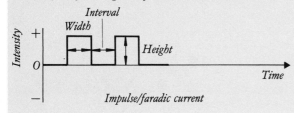

Impulse/faradic current

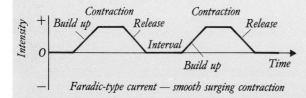

Faradic-type current — smooth surging contraction

65

Once the individual effects of each treatment are known, it becomes evident where in the treatment plan it can be used for maximum effect, and also where it is unsuitable for the individual, that is, it is termed contra-indicated.

CONTRA-INDICATIONS TO ELECTRICAL THERAPY

Electrical currents may only be used in beauty therapy when the client is healthy. In cases of poor or erratic health, or even a suspicion of illness, no treatment may be carried out, and the client must be directed to seek medical guidance. Contra-indications which prevent electrical therapy include:

(1) all existing and suspected diseases.
(2) all pain conditions.
(3) cases of inflammation or fever.
(4) history of thrombosis, especially using caution in areas where thrombosis has occurred. The treatment may only be contra-indicated in the legs or arms, etc., or may be generally inadvisable to apply. Medical guidance needed.
(5) all forms of tuberculosis, tumours, etc.
(6) any metal inserts, cardiac pacemakers, hip replacement joints, plates in bones.
(7) all areas with varicose veins protruding on the surface of the skin.
(8) areas of circulatory disorders, oedema (swelling, fluid retention), varicose ulcers, etc.
(9) pregnancy — no treatment in the abdominal and lower back areas. Special care generally in the first three months, preferably no treatment on any area of the body.
(10) the abdominal area during the first three days of menstruation. Additional care should be taken with intensity levels on body therapy throughout the period.
(11) regions with a reduced sense of feeling (hypaesthesia), because of the difficulty of assessing reaction.
(12) history of nervous illness, mental breakdown or acute depression. (Clients who live a highly tense or strained 'high stress' life should be treated with caution as their tolerance to electrical therapy may be very low. It may be wise to class clients undergoing treatment for stress from medical or para-medical sources as contra-indicated to beauty therapy treatment.)

HIGH-FREQUENCY CURRENT (H/F)

Some of the frequencies oscillate or alternate at such a rapid rate that they do not stimulate the sensory nerve endings, and are incapable of exciting muscle tissue, hence cannot cause a muscle

66

contraction. Their wave pattern is a rapidly swinging path, which alternates at a minimum of 500 000 Hz (cycles per second), so it is as its name suggests a really high or rapid frequency. Both the well-known high-frequency current in its direct and indirect forms, and short wave diathermy epilation current are of this type, and neither can excite muscle tissue or cause contractions. With H/F the current simply runs under the skin's surface and with short wave diathermy the residual current is dissipated or dispersed into the skin's tissues after the cautery of the hair follicle base has occurred.

So this current form has several effects — with H/F the beneficial effects are *stimulation, relaxation, drying germicidal actions* (direct H/F), with a destructive element also being present in the direct form when the H/F electrode is used as a probe. Although this aspect does not affect the therapist being confined to medical applications only, it does show that the high-frequency current can become a burning force if used incorrectly. So it should be used with care. Therapists should restrict the air gap — spark length — in direct applications to ½ cm (¼ in approximately) to avoid the destructive element causing skin irritation or damage. Modern H/F units, being of a high output, do not need to use this sparking technique with the direct method, but can obtain the same effect without breaking skin contact with the electrode, which is much more comfortable for the client.

High-frequency treatment can be applied by a direct or indirect method to create different effects, with the client becoming part of the circuit in the indirect method, and the current being induced directly on to the skin via glass electrodes with the direct method. The direct method provides drying, germicidal and skin-refining effects which can be used to good advantage on blemished or badly textured or scarred skins. Applied on a clean or lightly-talced skin, direct H/F provides a painless and clinical method of bringing fast relief to the acne sufferer, and is one of the most valuable treatments the therapist can offer. It is most effective when combined with galvanic desincrustation and vacuum suction treatment.

With the indirect method, the therapist draws the current indirectly through the client's skin to the fingers, altering the pressure of the hands to alter the result of the treatment. Light pressure creates a very stimulating surface effect, and firmer pressure causes a deeper vascular response in the tissues, followed by warmth and relaxation. These effects can be used on dry, lifeless complexions or where regeneration and deep relaxation is necessary in the mature client. In body treatments, for the tense nervous client, it can be applied within the heat therapy and massage routine, used as a reinforcement to the manual massage to soothe and relax tense muscle fibres, and improve the circulation.

MEDIUM-FREQUENCY CURRENTS — INTERFERENTIAL TREATMENT

As the rate of the oscillations or fluctuations of the alternating current decreases it is known as a medium-frequency current, and becomes capable of achieving muscle contractions. Interferential current falls into this category, with the muscular activity brought about by crossing two medium frequency currents in what is known as a superimposition field. The two electrode plates of the current are in diagonally opposed positions, and only the area in which the two currents cross causes an effect on the tissues (the superimposition field). For physiological reasons 1000 Hz has been selected as the dividing point between low and medium-frequency currents, and there are tremendous differences between them in terms of effect on the tissues. So each system has special applications related to effects, and the therapist must choose the treatment with her client's problem specifically in mind.

INTERFERENTIAL TREATMENT

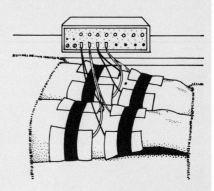

Interferential current provides a range of medium to low frequencies, all of which are applied through a four electrode system. The frequency 'tunes' itself to the client if applied correctly, and this makes for comfortable and effective biological and muscular activity when used on the medium frequencies, and effective clear but still smooth contractions on the lower more active frequency levels. The lower the frequency is, the slower the wave pattern becomes, and the contractions become stronger. Interferential current has a continuous wave pattern, with no pauses, so the client feels a surging wave-like sensation, which increases and decreases in intensity according to the 'beat' of the current.

With the interferential system of muscle activity, it is possible to work the area fully either to treat circulation problems such as cellulite, poor skin texture, crepey skin, etc., while dealing with the underlying problems of poor muscle tone, adipose deposits, etc. In the older client the circulatory-vascular fluid retention

conditions can be a major stumbling block to successful treatment, and these may require sorting out prior to the actual figure improvement treatment. It is not unusual to deal with clients who are the correct weight for their height and body type, but have specific reduction problems of heavy thighs and buttocks, or cellulite or slack skin tissues, etc., to mar their overall appearance. Medium-frequency currents provide an excellent, and sophisticated method of treating specific figure problems as well as general reduction and muscle toning conditions.

LOW-FREQUENCY CURRENTS — FARADISM

Low-frequency currents used for muscle contractions are based on the original principle of faradism, which was the current obtained from a faradic cell, so they are known as faradic-type currents, being a mixture of frequencies to improve comfort. The muscle contraction frequency is also widely known as an *impulse current,* and in fact many modern machines fall more into the medium-frequency range than low-frequency range to produce their muscle activity effects.

Modern equipment provides smooth contractions, where the current is surged or interrupted so that the action closely resembles natural exercise. This action trains the client's muscles to respond, and encourages client participation in home and clinic exercise routines to reinforce the electrical muscle contraction. If the client is extremely overweight or the muscles are suffering from disuse, possibly after injury or as a result of habitual postural faults, then faradism is an excellent aid to retraining the muscles to work. The client feels an immediate response and is encouraged.

Low-frequency currents are applied to the body in pairs of pads or electrodes to complete full body paddings. The low-frequency impulses are in the range 0 to 1000 Hz and permit active contractions on the muscles' motor points. Contractions are produced when sufficient current intensity is used, and this is surged or interrupted to allow relaxation of the muscles to produce a natural effect, similar to natural movements. The sensation the client experiences relates directly to the strength of the current, the impulse or period during which current is flowing, the interval or rest interruption between impulses or contractions, and the feel of the contraction (the time it takes to build up a contraction, which is affected by the shape of the wave form).

Electrodes/pads must not be moved while the treatment is in progress, and the intensity must be reduced if the pads need repositioning for comfort. Muscle contraction of the low-frequency type has current flowing very clearly between the two pads in each pair, if accurately placed. The current flows along the length of the muscles affecting the cells, nerves and muscle fibres. The current

69

also affects the skin, causing primary reactions, prickling under the pads, until a point or level of intensity where the current can flow clearly along the nerve path and cause stimulation of the muscle and a contraction to occur. To get to this more comfortable stage quickly, it is important to check motor point positions very carefully to save the client discomfort. If the pads are exactly in the correct position, the current is able to flow along the nerve path very quickly and is not diverted or reduced in power while attempting to reach the motor nerve. Lack of accuracy is the cause of discomfort very often with muscle toning routines.

MUSCLE CONTRACTION — THE EFFECTIVE WAY TO FIGURE SHAPING

One of the most popular methods of figure shaping is passive exercise, because it does not involve the client in much personal effort. Certainly, muscle contraction treatment through faradism or interferential systems is a valuable and profitable part of salon work if correctly applied.

It is at its best when offered as part of a combined programme. Saunas and steam baths, hydrotherapy air baths and pulsed showers before specific reduction treatments help to give improved results. The built-in heating aspect also assures that cm/in loss is achieved without discomfort, an important consideration if clients are not to be frightened off.

Specific reduction through muscle contraction needs the support of a reduced diet programme if overall weight loss is necessary. Muscle contraction works to tone and strengthen muscles and is most effective when used on clients within 7 to 14 kg (1 to 2 stone) of their correct weight, rather than as a treatment on those who are severely overweight.

This does not mean that it cannot be used on really overweight people, but its application is less effective. Other treatments such as heating routines, natural exercise and diet will be more useful initially. Muscle contraction does have a part to play in re-establishing awareness of muscle tone on obese people, but it may be difficult to apply effectively in many cases until the excess adipose tissue is shed through diet.

This point can often be used as an incentive on heavy clients to get them down to a size where muscle contraction techniques can be really instrumental in reshaping the body. Clients who need to reduce and reshape simultaneously will benefit most from muscle contraction and they are the ones who make up a large percentage of salon clients. So it is a service popular with them and profitable for you.

TREATMENT SYSTEMS

Muscle contraction systems from the various equipment manufacturers differ in their method of application and degree of comfort — but all work on the same principle of artificially stimulating the muscles into activity. Modern equipment is based on faradic-type currents, or interferential frequencies, which act in slightly different ways to produce muscular activity with associated vascular response in the area of treatment. So muscles can be strengthened and shortened, as they improve in tone, or even be built up slowly by muscle contraction applications.

From experience with clients it is possible to discover which systems act most effectively. Some systems of faradism seem more comfortable than others, with the surges of contraction appearing smoother. Much depends on good skin preparation and correct choice of system for individual body conditions. Equipment has improved so that less preparation time is needed to set up the treatment, which increases the use that can be made of sophisticated units — so justifying their cost. Maintenance is nominal if the equipment is well treated, and not moved unnecessarily. Gentle handling can prolong the life of muscle contraction units considerably, likewise if a unit is only used by one therapist who values it, and is aware of its worth to the clinic.

Some systems like the *Beauty Gallery* range have special trolleys which also house the leads and pads of the system, and these can be wheeled to where they are needed. This does save on wear and tear, on both the machine and the therapist! Multi-outlet units are available from all the major equipment companies. They range from the six outlet (12 pad) machines, which can be mains or battery operated, through to the ten or twelve outlet units which provide for 20 to 24 pads to be applied. Each outlet gives two pads to each electrode outlet, providing for a wider range of treatment possibilities. Interferential units are also available, using four electrodes, placed in diagonal patterns to produce the muscular activity. Special muscle contraction units are also available which are designed to be especially effective on the fluid retention 'cellulite' condition, and these normally have eight to ten outlets, giving 16 to 20 pads, of the normal graphite rubber type. Some of the really large clinic models provide facilities to alter the treatment's polarity, contraction rate, rest period, etc., and allow for a large range of muscular conditions to be treated very specifically. It is advisable to become competent and confident with the more basic units before progressing on to these more complicated machines, if accidents are not to occur. The less there is to control, the less likely it is that the treatment could be applied wrongly.

To start a muscle contraction service without a large initial outlay, it is possible to lease some of these units and this is proving

'BEAUTY GALLERY' SYSTEM

(a) The Beauty Gallery *with its faradic muscle contraction and body galvanic cellulite systems*

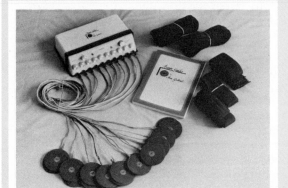

(b) The faradic system: ten outlet (20 pad), body straps (14), guide to muscle contraction

(c) The faradic unit: ten outlets, individually controlled on/off, pulse control, depth control, ready light, pulse light

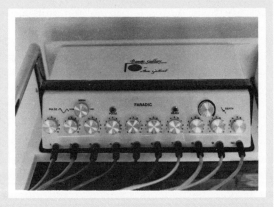

72

increasingly popular. Figure shaping treatment is so popular that the leasing cost of each unit is quickly recovered, and this does provide an instant way to get started in the profitable business of figure improvement. In many clinics the muscle contraction work accounts for more than half of the total body therapy completed, so it is a very important system to the clinics, and essential to offer for full success.

THE NEED FOR THE TREATMENT

The experienced beauty therapist will be able to recognize indications for treatment. Figure conditions which will benefit from faradism can be readily assessed at the initial figure diagnosis.

Figure reshaping, or a reduction of inches in one area of the body only, often termed spot reduction, is the most popular application. Treatment can also be given to help regain the figure after childbirth, for toning the pectoral muscles of the breasts, for shortening the rectus abdominis muscle to flatten the abdominal area, and to re-establish a waistline. It may also be given to firm and maintain a figure to avoid figure faults developing. In all these instances it is acting in the same way as natural exercise and is enhanced by the client following an exercise programme. However well applied electrical muscle contraction is, it is still passive exercise and can never match the overall circulatory and respiratory benefits of active exercise.

Once clients feel their muscles gaining in strength, their willingness to exercise increases, so therapists should always encourage additional activity. This improvement in awareness of physical health leads the client to value his or her appearance even more and increases clinic business overall through regular attendance. Not only then does the clinic get the credit for an improvement in the client's looks and health, it is also true therapy in action.

CONTRA-INDICATIONS

There are not many contra-indications to faradism because it is an action very close to natural movement, but there are instances where it should not be applied, or medical guidance should be sought.

Immediately before or during menstruation it is inadvisable and uncomfortable to treat the abdominal area. In early pregnancy it should not be applied, or after childbirth until medical permission is given. This would normally be after the postnatal examination (six to eight weeks after the birth), but would depend on the client's capacity for exercise as well, and the actual birth process itself, whether straightforward, or a difficult labour requiring longer recovery internally.

After operations, medical permission is again needed, and in the event of old scars in the treatment area, care should be taken to avoid discomfort if the skin has underlying adhesions or is taut.

A history of thrombosis or phlebitis (inflammation of the veins) recorded on the client's card would preclude treatment in the areas concerned. As a measure to prevent the formation of varicose veins it is excellent, although when protruding veins are established, treatment should not be used over them.

Any skin abrasions, open cuts, and so on, should be avoided. With a new client it is wise to check for skin sensation in the area to be treated. If a client has a loss of sensation in an area, they would be unable to guide the therapist as to comfortable levels of treatment. It might also point to a defect in the circulatory system such as swelling, oedema, and so on, which would contra-indicate the treatment. With older clients it is always a good idea to have them check with their doctors that they are suitable for muscle contraction. Then blood pressure, heart conditions, etc., are known about before the client starts treatment, which might well include other elements as well as faradism, such as heat therapy or lamp treatments.

HOW AND WHEN TO TREAT

The basic principle of muscle contraction is to copy natural muscle movements, so that muscles increase in tone, become stronger and more able to hold contours effectively. This is normally accomplished by working the muscles in groups, or occasionally in isolation, depending on the purpose of the treatment.

If general toning is required, a group or area placement of pads (electrodes) is used. They are placed in pairs, using alternating polarity, so that the entire area is activated. This achieves the same result as a period of active exercise, but is more specific, as it involves associated muscles less than natural exercise would. This means that it is not necessary to work for so long on any one area, as the effects of accurate muscle contraction are so concentrated.

In some cases where there are weak and disused muscles, muscular fatigue can be seen within 10 minutes of starting on exercising an area, and the treatment should be stopped, otherwise aching muscles and pain will be the result the next day. When unwilling muscles are being made to work, they tire very easily and they may require maximum current intensity even to get a response. As the muscles strengthen less current is needed to activate them and this gives a guide to the client's general progress.

Accuracy in pad placing is very important and will be individual to each client's body condition. The natural movement of the

METHODS OF PADDING

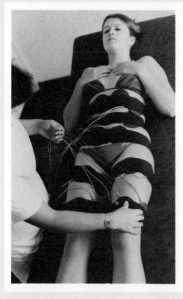

(a) Muscles work most clearly and comfortably when padded along their length, even when a general placing is applied, and multiple pads used

(b) An example of long axis padding on the quadriceps muscle of the thigh (along its length)

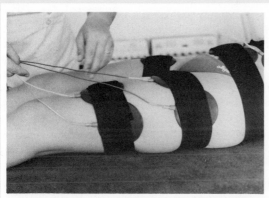

(c) A diagonal pad placing on the thigh, where the whole area becomes suffused with current intensity and works together. Motor point accuracy is vital, but pads are not paired along the muscles' length

75

muscles should be considered and pads placed to copy these movements as closely as possible. Initial diagnosis will show which figure problems can be helped by faradism or interferential applications. The purpose and actual method of treatment can also be decided. Breasts may need lifting and toning so the muscles need to be built in bulk to lift the breasts forward (pectoralis major and minor). The abdominal area may need flattening, so retraction movements are needed to draw in the abdominal wall, and tighten the rectus abdominis and oblique muscles. After childbirth the rectus abdominis may need shortening specifically to return it to normal. This is best accomplished by isolating it from the supporting muscles surrounding it, and initially contracting it longitudinally. This can be done with the point system, or by pad electrodes, using a fixed polarity, so that most of the contraction is in one direction.

Some clients may wish to add muscle bulk, to give their figure more shape, or simply keep it in trim. Male clients find it very useful to avoid thickening of the waistline, or to pull in a paunch caused by over-indulgence or lack of exercise.

ENSURING EFFECTIVE TREATMENT

For full success in all forms of muscle contraction it is necessary to have studied the body's muscular and skeletal systems in detail, to understand how they combine with the nervous system to form movement, and allow locomotion. A study of movement, *kinesiology,* examines how muscles work to achieve and maintain this natural locomotion. Every nerve and muscle, unless deeply covered by other muscles, possesses the capacity to be exercised artificially, on what is termed the *motor point*. This is an area which permits the clearest contraction, with the minimum use of current intensity, so making the treatment much more comfortable for the client. The motor points of the main muscles of the body should be known, as these are the muscles which determine the actual shape of the body, and will be the ones dealt with when applying faradism. Muscles which have no relationship to the bulk or shape of the body, can be learnt only after the main muscles are known, and the motor points have been traced. If pads are not positioned so that they can be effective on the muscles' motor points, the current is unable to make good contact, and is ineffective, and the treatment becomes uncomfortable to the client. There may be several areas on a muscle where a muscular response can be obtained, but they may not always be as comfortable as each other, so the well known motor points should always be tried first, before seeking different activity placings.

Several factors conspire to prevent clear motor point stimulation. Subcutaneous fat overlying the area acts as a barrier to the current,

76

MOTOR POINTS FOR ACTIVE CONTRACTIONS

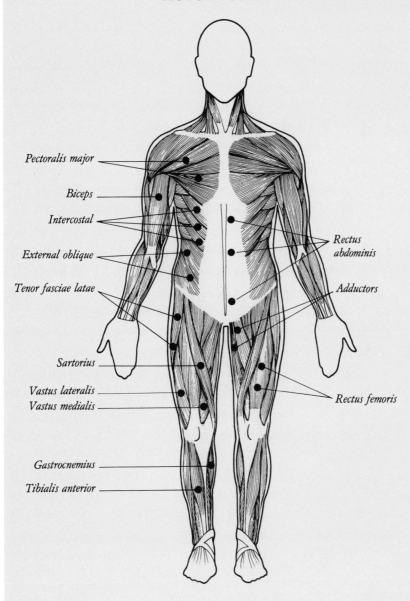

Pectoralis major

Biceps

Intercostal

External oblique

Tenor fasciae latae

Sartorius

Vastus lateralis

Vastus medialis

Gastrocnemius

Tibialis anterior

Rectus abdominis

Adductors

Rectus femoris

MOTOR POINTS FOR ACTIVE CONTRACTIONS

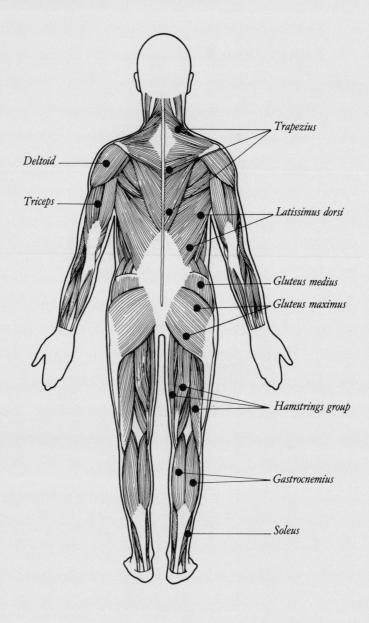

Trapezius

Deltoid

Triceps

Latissimus dorsi

Gluteus medius

Gluteus maximus

Hamstrings group

Gastrocnemius

Soleus

if present in large amounts, so accuracy of pad placing is vital in overweight clients. Poor skin preparation, adding to the natural resistance of the skin to the current, is another factor. Any oil left on the skin from oil massage will very effectively stop muscle contraction from taking place, and the client may have to take a shower to remove the remaining oil in the tissues. As this rather defeats the purpose of the routine, it is best to avoid combining faradism with any treatment that could add to the skin resistance.

The electrodes must be kept moist during treatment to form good contacts. The straps holding the pads in place must be firmly attached, so that the pads are in excellent contact with the skin, not floppy, or with their edges turned up so that only a percentage of the pads' surface is actually in contact.

The skin must be clean, free from oil or talc, and (ideally) should be moist to give the best medium for the current flow. Pre-heating saunas, steam baths or hydrotherapy units all help to make the

PADDING UP

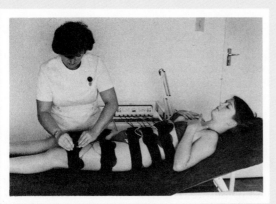

(a) Accurate placing of pads plus neat and firm strapping is vital for good results

(b) With colour-coded leads, pads needing adjustments during treatment can quickly be identified

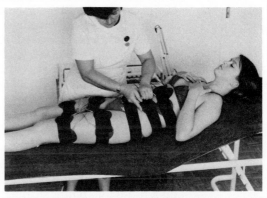

79

treatment more effective and comfortable, and should be advised for the client wherever possible. The warmth produced in the skin makes it possible to minimize the intensity (or amount) of current used, while still achieving excellent muscular response. This cuts down the client's sensation of the current which, initially, can be unnerving and uncomfortable if the client is tense or anxious.

This reaction to the primary sensation of the current is reduced with the interferential current system of treatment, due to the different principles of treatment involved. Minimized skin resistance, makes this a popular form of muscle contraction. With good skin preparation, however, all systems can be made to give excellent and comfortable treatments. It is up to the skill and efficiency of the therapist. Wiping over with soap and water if nothing else is possible and real attention to the natural motor points of the body, are far more important than following any chart of pad placings, or diagram of motor points.

PADDING THE CLIENT

Areas of the body to be treated can be padded up simultaneously if the muscles involved do not act as antagonists to each other. This saves time, and with independently controlled sets or pairs of electrodes, each area or muscle can be individually altered without unduly affecting connecting muscles.

Over-padding should be avoided as the treatment is not so effective, and the client may become anxious and tense, spoiling the treatment. It is preferable to perform a satisfactory contraction sequence on one area of muscles, working them fully and comfortably, and ending before fatigue sets in, then moving on to another area and repeating the process.

This may seem a lot of work, and not so attractive as padding up a client and leaving them. But therapists should remember that they are therapists, not technicians simply in control of a machine, and they should never underestimate the human factor when caring for the client undergoing faradism. Clients will quickly indicate they are unhappy with the treatment, by not returning for further sessions if they are not dealt with sympathetically.

A personally supervised treatment will give the client a feeling of security and by personally monitoring the progress of the contractions, more effective levels of muscular activity can be achieved. This means that the treatment will be more successful, the client will be able to recognize results quickly and be ready to recommend the salon and treatment to friends, and so help build up a profitable figure shaping business.

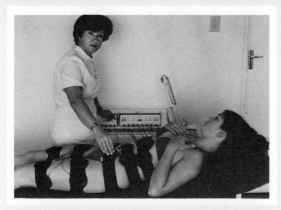

APPLYING TREATMENT

(a) Slip back the clear sleeving to separate leads and apply pads

(b) Three pairs of pads could be used on each thigh, leaving four pairs available for the abdominal area, or any other area needing treatment

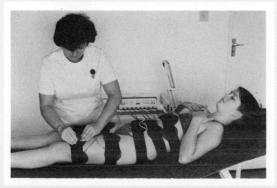

(c) Swiftly check all the pads for accuracy, contact and comfort, when the padding is complete

(d) Bring up contractions to an active level, check with the client for comfort and effect, reposition if necessary

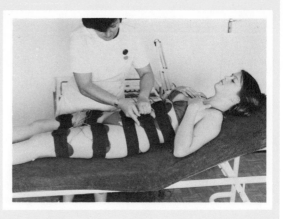

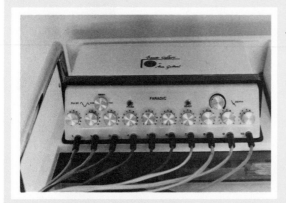

(e) The depth control can be used to provide extra power into the muscles, when needed

(f) As pads are removed, their clear sleeving is slipped back along the leads towards the pads to prevent tangling, and they are placed in order in the storage area on the Beauty Gallery *system*

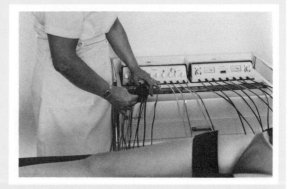

82

MASTER PLANS FOR PADDING LAYOUTS

Longitudinal padding system

Set 1 — exercises the pectoralis major and also involves the deltoid muscle thus causing movement of the shoulder

Set 2 — exercises the rectus abdominis very specifically and is ideal for shortening and flattening the abdominal muscles

Set 3 — exercises the oblique muscles and helps trim the waist

Set 4 — exercises the quadriceps muscles

Set 5 — supports this action and helps to tone the outside thigh area — useful in the case of adipose tissue deposits

Diagonal padding system

Set 1 — exercises the pectoralis major without involving the shoulder

Sets 2 and 3 together exercise the abdominal/midriff area as a group placing

Sets 4 and 5 together exercise the thigh generally

If necessary the inside thigh muscles (adductors) can be added to the group placing either with a split set, between both thighs, or closely placed as a pair directly over the muscles

The body is shown with different padding on both sides, either on the length of the muscles or in a diagonal placing to exercise a group of muscles

or an area of the body. The diagram is not an individual padding layout but suggests ways the muscles can be padded to accomplish effective muscle contractions

Muscles that are natural antagonists must NOT be exercised simultaneously

83

PADDING LAYOUTS FOR THE BACK OF THE BODY

Set 1 — shows a placing which is used to relieve tension in the trapezius muscle

Set 2 — shows a placing used as a reinforcement to prevent backache when there is a concentration of pads on the abdomen

Both sets 1 and 2 are termed split sets; that is the pads are split or divided between both sides of the body

Sets 3 and 6 are placed along the length of the muscles giving very clear contractions

Sets 4 and 5 together form a group placing for exercising the buttocks and thighs

Both layouts on each side of the body can be reinforced by more pads, following the same principles of diagonal or longitudinal padding

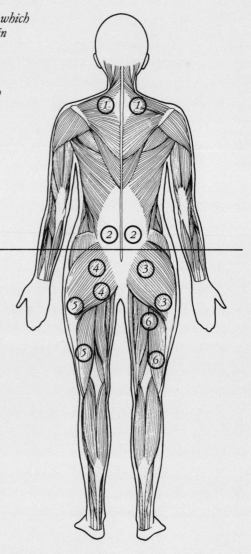

84

EXTRA PADDING LAYOUT SHEETS
— USE TO RECORD PADDING
LAYOUTS

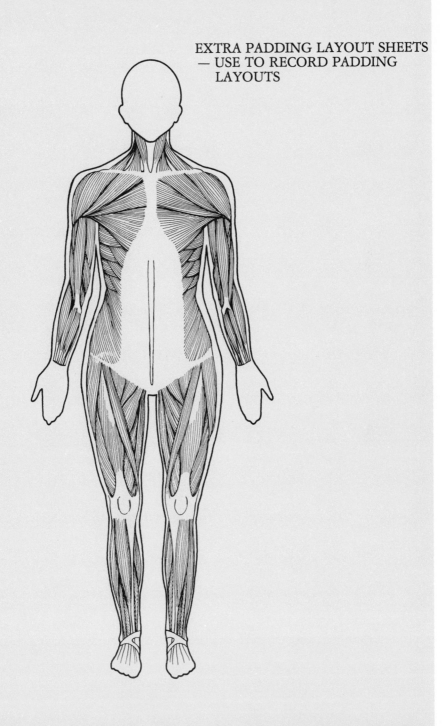

85

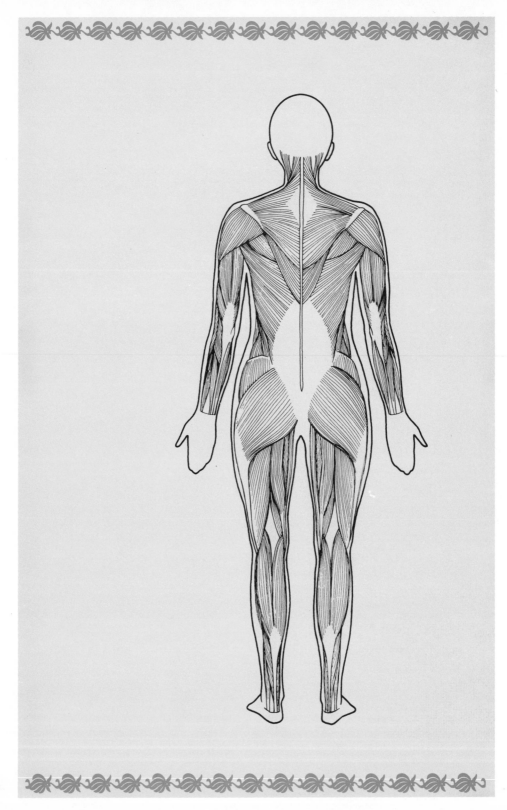

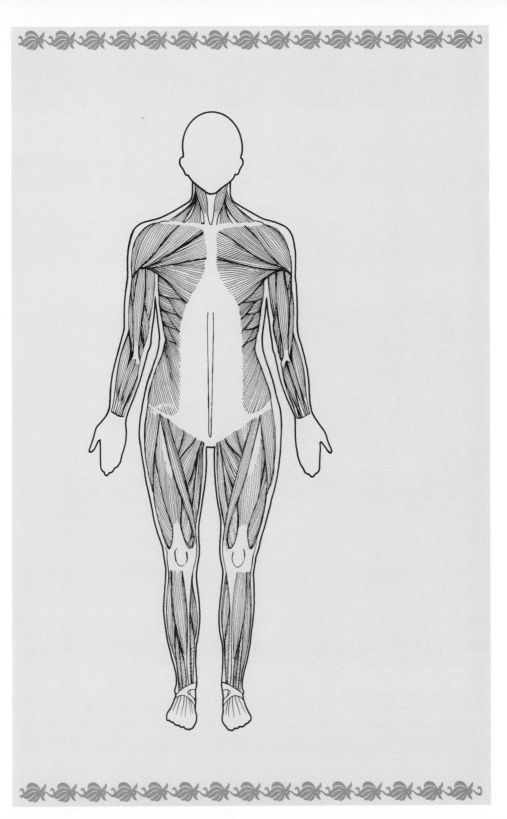

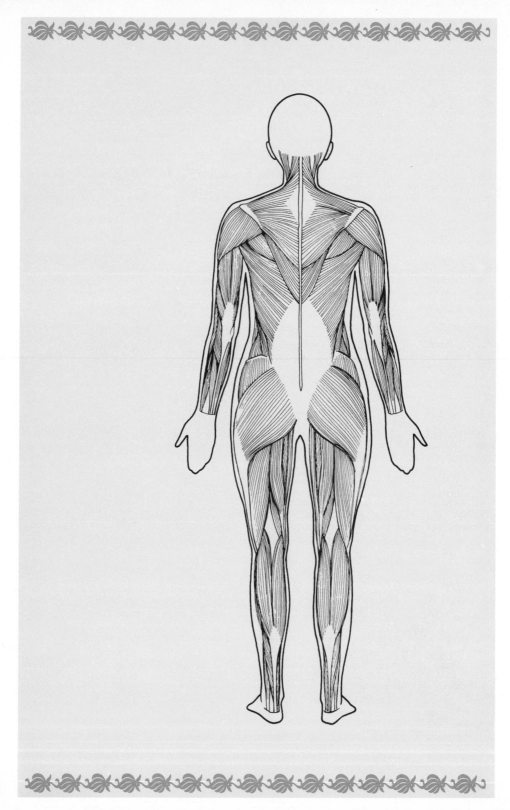

LYMPHATIC DRAINAGE MASSAGE
— VACUUM OR SUCTION TREATMENT

Lymphatic drainage massage is probably best explained as a form of massage where the main effects take place in the lymphatic system rather than by a direct application to it. It is a massage treatment designed to trace and follow the paths of venous and lymphatic systems of the body — either manually or by mechanical means.

It has been formulated over the years because of specific benefits to the body, both medically and aesthetically. Beauty therapy equipment for this kind of massage has been developed from the type of vacuum suction that was first used in hospitals for medical conditions where a suction effect was required, to draw up the tissues, and increase the circulation in the area.

Having once grasped the basic anatomy and physiology of the lymphatic system it is fairly easy to understand the effects that this kind of massage can have on the organs, systems and tissues of the body. Unlike certain other forms of massage, where scientific avenues are not yet fully understood, the effects of improving the flow of lymphatic fluids in the body can all be accounted for in physiological terms. In addition, there are many clients who prefer the sensation of vacuum massage, feeling it is likely to accomplish more for them physically. The gliding method if applied well can be a soothing routine, aided considerably if the client's tissues are warm from pre-heating, and also if they are kept warm during treatment.

EFFECTS OF LYMPHATIC DRAINAGE

Vacuum massage increases the lymphatic and vascular circulation — locally, and indirectly generally — if applied for a sufficient duration.

It increases dispersal of fluids in the tissues, if due to poor circulation, tiredness, etc.

It helps in adipose tissue dispersal within the body, if the client is on a reduced dietary intake.

Skin circulation can be improved, thus improving its texture, colour, and firmness.

THE LYMPHATIC SYSTEM

The lymphatic system comprises a network of knot-like vessels which contain valves to keep the fluids moving forwards and not being allowed to seep backwards. Along the course of these lymph vessels there are fluid filled nodules; these are known as glands or lymph nodes. The term nodes is more correct, because glands produce secretion which these lymph nodules do not. The nodes have no secretory function, but act as filters to prevent the spread of

SUPERFICIAL LYMPHATICS OF THE BODY

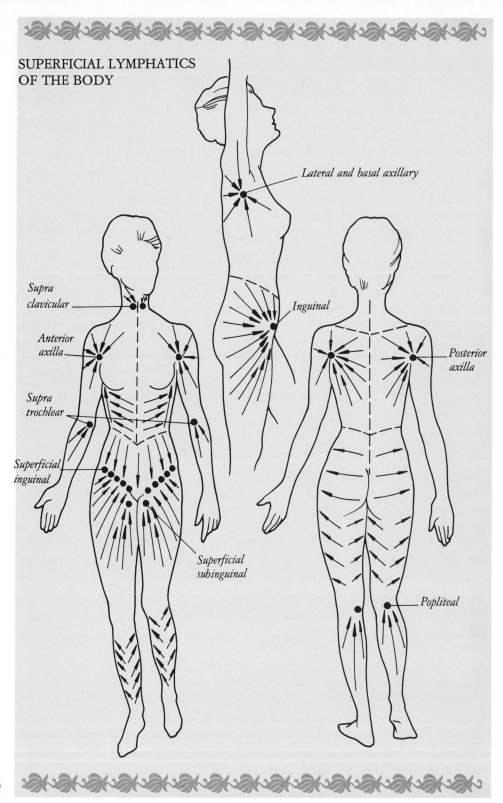

Lateral and basal axillary

Supra clavicular

Anterior axilla

Inguinal

Supra trochlear

Posterior axilla

Superficial inguinal

Superficial subinguinal

Popliteal

infection in the body. Following the course of the veins, the lymphatic drainage is usually aimed at the superficial set, although this in turn affects the deeper vessels. The superficial vessels lie in the superficial fascia which is a connective tissue membrane embracing all structures of the body and is immediately beneath the skin. When the superficial lymphatic vessels become inflamed, red streaks appear on the skin and the lymph nodes also swell. Two main large ducts drain the lymph from the lymphatic vessels and open into the venous system at the root of the neck. However, some lymphatic vessels, especially in the limbs, open directly into their nearby veins. Important groups of lymph nodes are gathered together at varying points on the body. So it is necessary to consider the relevant lymph nodes and the areas they drain into when attempting to treat this system by massage.

Lymph (from the latin word lympha, meaning 'spring water') is the fluid contained in the lymphatic vessels. It is a clear fluid formed from the tissues which has seeped from the capillary walls and contains mainly water and salts. The function of the lymph is to carry away the products of metabolism and chemical change from the tissues, such as carbon dioxide, lactic acids, bacteria and some of the fat after digestion. The flow of lymph largely depends upon respiration and general active exercise. It is directly affected by inactivity, rest, and sedentary occupations. Tissue fluids accumulate when the flow of lymph is retarded.

Several conditions result from the accumulation of tissue fluids. These are mainly swelling, oedema, etc., which may be readily relieved by massage if the problem is not a medical one, or relates to a systemic condition of the body, which would contra-indicate the routine.

CONTRA-INDICATIONS

There are several reasons why vacuum suction may not be applied, some local, others more general. If for any reason fluid accumulations might be thought to relate to a medical condition, seek medical advice through the client's doctor.

Contra-indications include:

(1) over the breasts, or abdomen in pregnancy.

(2) during menstruation on the abdominal area.

(3) over varicose veins, inflamed skin, bites, etc.

(4) over hypersensitive skin.

(5) directly over scar tissue, as it is less able to stretch.

GENERAL POINTS OF TREATMENT

The treatment should be applied in a rhythmical fashion, using a cup size suited to the area. The cup must make good contact, otherwise a vacuum is not created and the tissues are not lifted in the cup effectively, so reducing the overall effect. The amount of lift into the cup (the reduced pressure) can be altered in several ways to create a good result without discomfort. The speed of the strokes can be varied, made slower or faster, thus increasing or decreasing the effect of the vacuum or lift into the cup. The actual cup size can be altered, a small cup having far less effect than a large one. Lastly the actual vacuum level can be altered on the machine, which reduces the pressure and alters the degree of lift into the cup of the subcutaneous tissues.

With practice, skilled therapists find that they tend to vary the treatment to suit the individual, more by altering their speed of strokes, than by constantly changing the clear cups used, as this is a time-consuming task and rather breaks the flow of the treatment. Also if a large area of the body can be cleared for treatment this also helps the flow of the routine, and permits a more effective treatment to be completed. The buttocks and back thighs area for example, can normally be treated together, perhaps for half an hour in some cases, giving a concentrated effect that will certainly provide results if the client is also losing weight generally.

Keeping the client really warm also maximizes the results obtained. Pre-heating should be used, general or specific such as lamps, and these can be kept in position during and after the vacuum routine. As an area is completed, it can be wrapped to retain the vascular increase created for as long as possible. On many occasions when therapists consider that they do not get good results from vacuum treatments, it is because they are not applying them in the way they need to be used to have a real effect on the lymphatic system.

VACUUM
SUCTION

(a) Back thigh

(b) On back

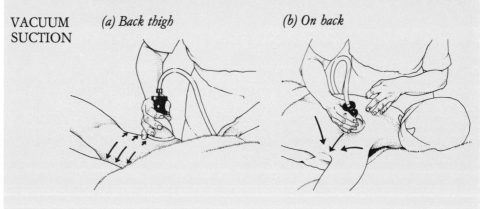

92

8

Galvanic cellulite treatments

One of the most common figure problems among clients is cellulite, a condition of defective circulation associated in most cases with localized weight accumulation. Cellulite could be considered a form that fat takes in certain areas of the body, and should be dealt with in that way, needing a special approach, just as any other difficult body condition does.

Galvanic current can be put to good use in the treatment of cellulite, either for localized problem areas such as the thighs, using 4 pads, or for generalized conditions using a complete body cellulite system with up to 16 paired pads being applied simultaneously to save time. Galvanic current, either used independently or within a combined cellulite routine of 1 hour, works very effectively on cellulite on the thighs, buttocks, or abdominal areas, and is especially useful where specific reduction in one area is needed.

HOW GALVANISM WORKS

The principles of galvanism for treating cellulite are, however, identical whether 4 or 16 pads/electrodes are used, being based on iontophoresis or penetration of active substances into the tissue to speed fluid loss from the tissues and help the mobilization of fat when the client is on a reduction diet. The client's shape can alter because of the fluid loss even without a change in the overall weight.

Each set of pads or electrodes act as a pair with differing polarities, one acts as positive, one as negative. The positive electrode is marked by a red connection wire, the negative electrode by a black wire attaching it to the galvanic unit's outlet connection. So one pad acts as the indifferent electrode, the other as the working active electrode, though this polarity can be altered on the machine to change the attracting force of the electrode. It can be designated positive or negative in its polarity according to the effects required, by altering the polarity changer on the galvanic unit.

BODY GALVANIC CELLULITE — FULL BODY APPLICATION

(a) Full body treatment of cellulite provides fast, effective and profitable results for the clinic

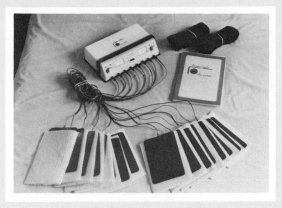

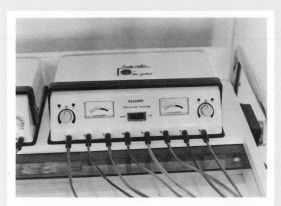

(b) With eight outlets (16 pads) many cellulite problem areas can be treated at once

(c) The cellulite treatment is very popular with clients as it gives them the results they want

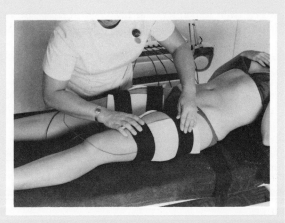

94

> There is no international convention of colour coding leads on galvanic equipment. If using equipment other than the kind described in this guide, then therapists must consult the equipment manufacturer to determine which lead acts as positive at the start of treatment.

The process of galvanic iontophoresis for cellulite in body therapy is very similar to the penetration of active substances in facial therapy. What does differ is the nature of the lotions, emulsions, gels, etc., being applied to treat the cellulite condition, and the action on the cellular tissues to aid the removal of the cellulite problem.

CELLULITE

This is a body condition of ineffective circulation, normally associated with an adipose or fatty tissue deposit in a localized area, which assumes a dimpled skin appearance on compression. It is a very unattractive body problem which can spoil an attractive figure, so the galvanic treatment is a very popular application which can produce excellent results if reinforced by the client's efforts at home. It is a condition considered to be associated with poor body elimination, an inability of the body system to get rid of toxic substances, and a general lack of vitality in the body. It is a problem condition in that it can affect very active people who exercise regularly and are fit, as well as sedentary individuals who do not lead a very healthy or vigorous existence.

Factors such as constipation, incorrect diet (too high in fats, carbohydrates, alcohol), smoking, lack of exercise and deep and correct breathing, effects of stressful living, poor sleeping patterns, etc., are all considered to have a bearing on the condition. So a full body assessment is needed to resolve the problem. Probably the most important factor overall is elimination, aided by a fruit and vegetable and protein diet (classed as an elimination type of diet), and factors which speed the release of the fluids trapped in the cell membranes of the subcutaneous fatty tissue layers. So galvanic treatment is excellent for the problem of cellulite, having a flushing effect on the system when used in combination with anti-cellulite products which have a diuretic effect for example 'Cellulite Lotion' from the Gallery Line 'Jade' body range.

The diuretic or fluid loss effect caused by the penetration of the active lotions under the active pads, causes the client to pass more fluid as urine, and stubborn areas of cellulite disperse over a period of time. The client must have medical advice as to the suitability of the treatment if they have a medical history of kidney infections,

infections of the bladder or urinary tract, as the treatment can cause irritation on rare occasions due to the active substances the body is passing through in the urine. The client should be warned about the additional water they will pass, so that they do not become anxious. The effect will be accelerated if the client uses an anti-cellulite product on the problem area at home, and is also drinking herbal teas to speed the elimination process.

APPLICATION

The galvanic cellulite treatment can be applied independently over a clean skin (normally washed and rinsed thoroughly), or used within a 1 hour cellulite routine, incorporating peeling, heat, massage, muscle contraction or vacuum suction, and galvanism/iontophoresis. This treatment is extremely effective in the removal of the cellulite problem, which can be considered a special type of weight condition. The combination of stimulation, circulation improvement, interchange of blood and lymphatic fluid effects caused by the heat, massage, lymphatic drainage (vacuum) applications, is then flushed away by the effect of the galvanic current penetrating the diuretic, anti-cellulite product into the tissues. The effect of this action when linked with the pumping effect of the faradic current on the muscles as they are exercised, is very effective in removing areas of stubbon adipose tissue.

The galvanic current plays an important part in this overall elimination process, both by the product penetration, and by causing an interchange of tissue fluids within the cell membrane. It is considered that the galvanic application would still be effective without the cellulite product because of this interchange effect, but it seems more effective to involve the client in their progress and improvement of the problem. It also centres their attention on to the offending area, and results do appear to be obtained more quickly when a product is applied within the treatment, and used at home. The client is made more aware of the treatment's effects on their body, and it also gets them more involved in the whole treatment programme, which is excellent. The client can be shown how to use massage movements on the problem area, when applying the product at home, and they may be encouraged to use a friction glove with body wash/shower products, all elements known to aid the circulation and tone the skin.

THE CELLULITE ROUTINE

The 1 hour cellulite routine is a very impressive and effective treatment for cellulite, and is popular with clients because of the results which can be obtained in reshaping the figure. It has become a standard part of body therapy, and should be offered wherever a full body service is available.

CELLULITE ROUTINE — PEELING AND PREPARATION

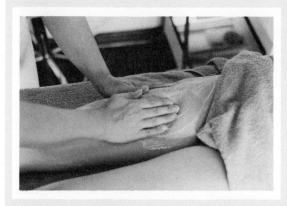

(a) The working area is protected, and a thin film of body peeler is applied to the cellulite affected area and worked into a thin lather

(b) Brisk rolling, friction movements used to stimulate the circulation and deep clean the skin, to break down skin resistance to electrical current

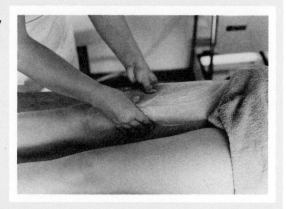

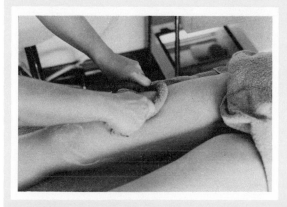

(c) The peeler is removed with hot towels, wrung out and twisted into loops to allow fast cleansing of the area. Rinse and repeat briskly until all traces of peeler are gone

97

MASSAGE AND HEAT

(a) Massage in the form of petrissage and compression movements is used to hasten elimination. Working gently initially to avoid discomfort on the cellulite areas

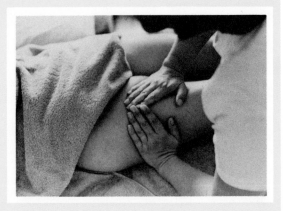

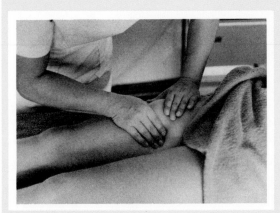

(b) Deep kneading is used firmly and deeply to improve biological functioning in the area, and speed dispersal of the cellulite condition

(c) Effleurage, stroking movements are used to link strokes and relieve any discomfort or spasm in the muscles. Heat lamps and vacuum massage can be used to vary the routine

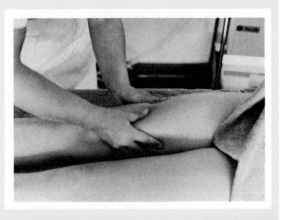

MUSCLE CONTRACTION/GALVANIC CELLULITE TREATMENT

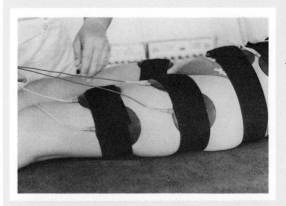

(a) The oil is removed very thoroughly, the area is washed and muscle contraction applied, working to clear motor point placings along the length of the muscles. Only 10 minutes of active contractions needed

(b) The faradic pads are removed and an anti-cellulite product massaged thoroughly into the skin, particularly in the areas where the damp galvanic pads are to be applied

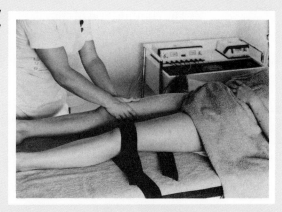

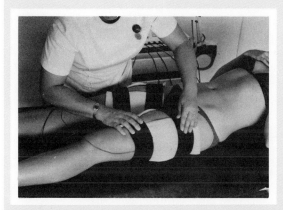

(c) The paired galvanic pads are applied in their envelopes, placing the active pad over the worst areas. The negative pole is applied for 5 to 6 minutes, adjusted to client comfort, polarity returned to zero and positive pole used for 3 to 4 minutes. So treatment starts with the black lead going to the working pad (cellulite area) and red lead going to the indifferent pad acting as the magnet

99

Concentrated cellulite applications can be designed to meet the client's specific needs, based on the information gained from the figure assessment. The routine can be adapted to give more time to muscle contraction, less to massage, etc., according to the state of the body, degree of muscle tone, amount of fluid retained, etc., and existing contra-indications. If elimination is a problem then galvanism can be given prominence in the application, and advice given to help elimination by changes in life style, exercise, diet, etc.

As these are active and effective routines, there will be a small proportion of clients who will get a reaction to the treatment, even with careful checking of contra-indications and medical guidance, so it is wise to apply the treatment with caution initially, until the client's reactions are known. The treatment programme must be sensibly controlled by the therapist, who is responsible for her client's well being, and not decided by the client, who will want to push in as much treatment as possible, once its effectiveness is noted.

The combination of stimulating the circulation, and then flushing the system to take full effect of the dietary changes occurring in the body, works very effectively on most clients. It is important to realize that the galvanic application does not need to be actually felt by the client to be effective, it works at a level below which the client is aware of any sensation. Applying the galvanic current at a low level provides the desired penetration action, but reduces side effects of skin irritation, soreness, etc., which can occur.

TREATMENT CONCLUSION

The damp galvanic pads in their envelopes are removed, and a few minutes' massage concludes the routine, to aid dispersal of lactic acid in the tissues. The cellulite product is not rinsed away but left in the skin to continue its effects. The client can be advised to use the cellulite products at home to keep the action going, and to maintain the diuretic effects on the body. Suitable products include Body Peeler, Body Wash, Massage Oil, Body Lotion and Cellulite Lotion from the *Gallery Line Jade Body Range* by Ann Gallant.

PLANNING THE CELLULITE PROGRAMME

Cellulite treatments, like all body routines, need to be applied regularly for success, and should be promoted as a plan of 10 to 12 treatments, whether the 1 hour cellulite routine is applied or the ½ hour galvanic application is given independently.

With the larger galvanic cellulite systems, it is advisable to treat the body only once a week until the effects are known. If no adverse results occur, the routine can be applied twice weekly if the problem is a major one. Or, the 1 hour cellulite routine can be interspaced in the slimming plan with associated treatments such as ½ hour muscle contraction, vibratory massage, etc., which reinforce the effects that are not so directly connected with fluid loss from the body.

Factors that will help the therapist in her treatment planning include the client's age, overall size, general health, and contra-indications. Contra-indications may limit the range of applications in older women, especially circulatory problems, high blood pressure, varicose veins, etc., and clients must know the state of their health before commencing treatment.

For further information on galvanic body treatments, see *Beauty Guide 3: Galvanic Treatment,* by Ann Gallant.

The use of home advised products is essential for success on the cellulite condition

Useful Addresses

PROFESSIONAL ORGANIZATIONS AND EXAMINATION BOARDS

Further information on courses is available from the following examination boards and professional organizations:

Aestheticians' International Association Inc,
5206 McKinney, Dallas, Texas, USA

American Electrolysis Association,
Corresponding Secretary Sandi Strum, 211 Jonnet Building,
4099 William Penn Highway, Monroeville P.A. 15146, USA

Beauty Education International — Beauty Club
Ann Gallant, Forum, Stirling Road, Chichester PO19 2EN, UK

E A Ellison & Co Ltd, Brindley Road South,
Exhall, Coventry CV7 9EP, UK

Esthetic and Beauty Supply, 16 Coldwater Road, Don Mills,
Ontario M3B 1Y7, Canada Tel (416) 444 1154
There is also a Californian office, USA

British Association of Beauty Therapy and Cosmetology,
Secretary Mrs D. Parkes, Suite 5, Wolesley House,
Oriel Road, Cheltenham GL50 1TH, UK

British Association of Electrolysis,
16 Quakers Mead, Haddenham, Bucks HP17 8EB, UK

British Biosthetic Society,
2 Birkdale Drive, Bury, Greater Manchester BL8 2SG, UK

City and Guilds of London Institute,
46 Britannia Street, London WC1 9RG, UK

**Le Comité Internationale D'Esthétiques et de Cosmetologie,
(CIDESCO),**
CIDESCO International Secretariat, PO Box 9, A1095 Vienna,
Austria

Confederation of Beauty Therapy and Cosmetology,
Education Secretary Mrs B. Longhurst, 3 The Retreat, Lidwells
Lane, Goudhurst, Kent, UK

Institute of Electrolysis,
251 Seymour Grove, Manchester M16 0DS, UK

International Aestheticians' Association,
2304 Monument Boulevard, Pleasant Hill, California 94523,
USA

National Federation of Health and Beauty Therapists,
PO Box 36, Arundel, West Sussex BN18 0SW, UK

International Therapy Examination Council,
3 The Planes, Bridge Road, Chertsey, Surrey KT16 8LE, UK

The Northern Institute of Massage,
100 Waterloo Road, Blackpool FY4 1AW, UK

Skin Care Association of America,
16 West 57th Street, New York, NY, USA

South African Institute of Health and Beauty Therapists,
PO Box 56318, Pinegowrie 2123, South Africa

EQUIPMENT MANUFACTURERS

Ann Gallant Beauté Therapy Equipment,
Esthetic and Beauty Supply, 16 Coldwater Road, Don Mills,
Ontario M3B 1Y7, Canada, Tel (416) 444 1154
There is also a Californian office, USA

Beauty Gallery Equipment by Ann Gallant,
E. A. Ellison & Co Ltd, Brindley Road South,
Exhall, Coventry CV7 9EP, UK, Tel (0203) 362505

Colne Development Co Ltd,
2 Station Road, Twickenham, Middlesex, UK

Cristal (Equipment),
86 Rue Pixérécourt, 75020 Paris, France

Depilex Ltd and Slimaster Beauty Equipment Ltd,
Regent House, Dock Road, Birkenhead, Merseyside L41 1DG,
UK

Electro-Medical Services,
Bermuda Road, Nuneaton, Warks, UK

George Solly Organization Ltd,
James House, Queen Street, Henley on Thames, Oxon, UK

Soltron Solarium and Sun Beds,
Josef Kratz, Vertriebsgesellschaft mbH Rottbitzer Straße
69–5340 Bad Honnef 6 Tel 02224/818-0 Telex jk 8861194

Nemectron Belmont Inc,
17 West 56th Street, New York, NY10019, USA

Silhouette International Beauty Equipment,
Kenwood Road, Reddish, Stockport, Cheshire SK5 6PH, UK

Slendertone Ltd,
12–14 Baker Street, London W1M 2HA, UK

Taylor Reeson Ltd,
96–98 Dominion Road, Worthing, Sussex, UK

TREATMENT PRODUCT SUPPLIERS

Ann Gallant Beauté Therapy Products,
Esthetic and Beauty Supply, 16 Coldwater Road, Don Mills,
Ontario M3B 1Y7, Canada
There is also a Californian office, USA

Elizabeth of Schwarzenberg,
13 Windsor Street, Chertsey, Surrey KT16 8AY, UK

Clarins (UK) Ltd,
(Oils and body products)
150 High Street, Stratford, London E15 2NE, UK

Gallery Line by Ann Gallant, Skin Care and Body Products,
E. A. Ellison & Co Ltd, Brindley Road South,
Exhall, Coventry CV7 9EP, UK Tel (0203) 362505

Pier Augé Cosmetics,
Harbourne Marketing Associates, Oak House,
271 Kingston Road, Leatherhead, Surrey, UK

Thalgo Cosmetic/Importex,
(Marine based products)
5 Tristan Square, Blackheath, London SE3 9UB, UK

MAGAZINES AND TRADE PUBLICATIONS

Beauty Club by Ann Gallant
(International club for all those involved in the beauty industry —
publications/fact sheets/guides/books, etc.)
Details from:
Beauty Education International, Forum, Stirling Road,
Chichester PO19 2EN, UK
Telex 86402, CHITYP G. Ref GALLANT

Ellison, Brindley Road South, Exhall Trading Estate,
Exhall, Coventry, UK Tel 0203 362505

Esthetic and Beauty Supply, 16 Coldwater Road, Don Mills,
Ontario M3B 1Y7, Canada Tel (416) 444 1154
There is also a Californian office, USA

Health and Beauty Salon Magazine

Hair and Beauty Magazine

Hairdresser's Journal

Trade publications for the Hair and Beauty Industries,
details from International Business Press, Quadrant House,
The Quadrant, Sutton, Surrey, UK
(Health and Beauty Salon Magazine Editor — Ms Marion
Mathews) Tel 01 661 3500